Hillel's Calendar

By MAMIE G. GAMORAN

Illustrated by IDA LIBBY DENGROVE

Published by UNION OF AMERICAN HEBREW CONGREGATIONS
New York

Hillel's
Calendar

● TISHRI ~ OCTOBER ●

SUN	MON	TUES	WED	THURS	FRI	SAT
				1	2 * ROSH HA-SHONO 3	
4	5	6	7	8	9	10
11 * YOM KIPPUR 12		13	14	15	16 SU.	
18	19	20	22	2	SERES	
25	2	27	2	29	30	31

*Jewish holiday begins at sundow

UNION GRADED SERIES

EDITED BY

RABBI EUGENE B. BOROWITZ, *Director of Education*

UNION OF AMERICAN HEBREW CONGREGATIONS

Library of Congress Catalogue Card Number: 60–10180

Copyright, 1960

UNION OF AMERICAN HEBREW CONGREGATIONS

PRODUCED IN U.S. OF AMERICA

TO MY DEAR GRANDCHILDREN

Sammy

Benjy

AND

Joseph

Adam

AND

Saul

Joshua

Editor's Introduction

How pleasant it is to welcome back an old friend! It is none other than Hillel who has for so many years delighted Jewish children and parents with his joyous celebration of the Jewish holidays.

He has returned in *Hillel's Calendar* not only to give us additional insights into the great events of the Jewish year but to bring us something of the spirit which unites them month after month in the cycle of the Jewish year. Surely, children who have come to love this friendly companion of their early childhood will enjoy seeing him a year later reacting in a more mature way to the sights and sounds, the meaning and inspiration of the Jewish and American holidays.

And is this not one of our major aims in Jewish education, to show the continuing value of the Jewish way of life as we grow in age and wisdom? For children and adults alike the meaning of Judaism cannot be confined to a single level of interpretation. Rather, as our single lives seek their interpretation through continuing celebrations of Judaism's and America's special days, we are made aware of how much there is yet to learn and to be.

To bring our children some sense of continuing Jewish growth and development in this blessed land is one of the major aims of this sequel to *Hillel's Happy Holidays*. That it may have success in implanting this lesson in the hearts of our children is our earnest hope, as once again we send Hillel forth into the great wide world.

RABBI EUGENE B. BOROWITZ
Director of Education

Acknowledgments

I wish to express my thanks to the members of the Reading Committee of the Commission on Jewish Education, Rabbi Leon Fram, Rabbi Sidney M. Lefkowitz, and Rabbi Lawrence W. Schwartz, for their careful reading of the manuscript and for many helpful suggestions.

My thanks are also offered to Mr. Ralph Davis who designed and produced the book. Its fine format bears testimony to his good taste and authority in the field of book-making. I am grateful, too, to Mrs. Julia Minor who was always ready to assist in the preparation of the manuscript and to Miss Sylvia Schiff who guided it through galleys and page proof.

This was the first manuscript which I submitted to the new editor and director of the Commission on Jewish Education, Rabbi Eugene B. Borowitz. It is a pleasure to acknowledge his kind cooperation as well as the many excellent comments he made for the improvement of the book.

Hillel's Calendar may be called a "directive" from readers of *Hillel's Happy Holidays*. There were so many letters asking for "more stories about Hillel," that they could not be denied. I hope the readers will enjoy the new stories. I shall be especially pleased if from them, our boys and girls will begin to realize the common traditions of their American and Hebraic background.

M.G.G.

New York, May, 1960

Contents

Hillel's Calendar

Introducing Hillel

Do you remember Hillel? We met him in *Hillel's Happy Holidays*. We read about his holiday adventures.

Many boys and girls wrote letters. They asked, "What is Hillel doing now? Are there any more stories about him?"

Of course there are more stories about him. You will find them in this book.

Hillel is a little older now. He is almost nine years old. His brother Joseph is twelve and his little sister Leah is going on six. They still live together with Mother and Father in their big white house. His friend, Stanley, still lives in the red house next door. And they all visit with Cousin David very often.

Now let us share some more happy holidays with Hillel.

The New Calendar

It was just a few days before Rosh Ha-shono. Hillel came home early from school. Mother said, "The house must be clean and shining for the holiday. Will you help me? Please look in your closets and in your drawers. I am sure you will find odds and ends tucked into corners. Fill your wastebasket with old papers and pencil stubs and soiled blotters. We shall throw them all away. Examine your shirts and sweaters. If any are too small for you, bring them to me. We can give them away to a boy or girl who can wear them."

Hillel went right to work. He was surprised at what he found in his desk. He hated to part with some things, but he knew there was nothing else to do. First he opened the top drawer. It was full of scraps of crayons and tiny stubs of pencils and paper clips that were out of shape. He found an old silver whistle. He tried it out. It didn't blow any more. That would have to go. From the lowest drawer he drew out a whole package of drawings left over from last year. They were smudged and dirty. He didn't

need them any more. Before he knew it, his waste-basket was full and his desk was clean. He opened his closet and straightened out his clothes. There was nothing to give away. Everything was still big enough for him to wear.

He came downstairs to Mother. "Give me another job," he said, "I am finished in my room."

"Good," said Mother. "I do have another job for you. Please open this package."

The package was a small cardboard box. It opened on two ends. Hillel opened them and a small book slid out. He turned the pages carefully. It seemed to be a sort of calendar. But it was different from the calendars he was used to seeing. Usually the calendar hung on the wall. This calendar was made to stand or lie on a desk. Another difference was that this calendar had Hebrew and English printed on every page. And this calendar began in the middle of September. It was a puzzle.

"What is this little book, Mother?" he asked. "I don't think I ever saw one like it before."

"Perhaps not," Mother answered. "It is a Hebrew calendar. We call it a *luach*. Daddy keeps it in his desk in the top drawer. Please put it there for me."

Hillel was not satisfied. He wanted to know

more about the Hebrew calendar. "I didn't know there is a special Hebrew calendar. Why do we need it?"

"How would we know about the Jewish holidays without a calendar? To keep all our dates in order, we need an English calendar and a Hebrew calendar," Mother replied. "I have a special calendar, too, something like Daddy's. The temple Sisterhood sends it to me every year at Rosh Ha-shono time. It is very useful. It shows all the important Jewish and English dates in the year."

"There must be a lot to know about the Hebrew calendar," said Hillel. "I'll ask Daddy tonight. Joseph and Leah will want to hear it, too. He will explain it to us." Then Hillel had another thought. "Maybe there is a story to tell. Two calendars must have at least one story."

7

The Little Shepherd

The family was just finishing their dinner. Mother was bringing in the dessert. It was sponge cake with strawberry sauce. Everyone liked it.

Hillel waited until everyone was served. This was the best time to ask questions and to tell about things that happened during the day. He was thinking about the new calendar.

"We are very lucky," said Hillel. "We celebrate Washington's Birthday and Columbus Day and Fourth of July. But that's not all. We celebrate Purim, Pesach and Shovuos and other Jewish holidays."

"What a lot of holidays," Leah put in. Leah was growing up. Her hair was brown and curly. She wore a plastic band across it with a colored bow at the side. The bow usually matched her dress. Mother had a large assortment of ribbons for Leah. Tonight she wore a yellow dress and a yellow ribbon. Hillel thought she looked very pretty.

"That's why we need two calendars," Joseph explained. "Otherwise we would not know on which day the holidays come each year."

"We might celebrate Chanuko on the Fourth of July and Purim on Thanksgiving," said Hillel.

This made Leah giggle. "Let's have Purim for eight days like Chanuko," she said. "I would like that best."

"Then we should have three calendars," said Joseph. "One will be an English calendar, one will be a Hebrew calendar, and one will be Leah's calendar."

"What is all this talk about calendars?" asked Father.

"This is what happened," explained Hillel. "Rosh Ha-shono is coming. Mother gave me a new calendar to put in your desk. I was looking at it. It shows the days and the weeks and the months. It shows the Jewish holidays and the American holidays. It is printed in Hebrew and in English. This is the first time I saw that kind of calendar. Please tell us about it."

"You must mean the luach," said Father. "That will take a long time. Does everyone have plenty of time?"

"Oh, yes," said Joseph. "We have done our homework for school. We have time to listen."

"Let us help Mother clear the table," said Father. "Then I will tell you about the calendars."

9

10

Everyone helped. Mother went into the kitchen. Joseph and Father carried in the dishes. Leah carried in all the silver. Hillel picked up the glasses. He put them on a tray and carried it very carefully. Father came back and took the tablecloth off the table. Joseph swept the dining-room floor with the carpet sweeper. In a jiffy the dining-room was in order.

"Thank you," said Mother. "You may all go into the study with Father. It will not take me long now to wash the dishes. You have all helped."

The children went into the study with Father. Father sat down on the big chair. The children sat on the floor. Father began.

"Try to think back long, long ago. We will think about a shepherd boy. His name was Marneen. He lived in Palestine at the time of King David. Marneen had to get up early in the morning. He would take out the sheep to graze in the fields. Marneen did not have a clock to wake him in the morning."

"The sun would wake him up," cried Joseph.

"Yes," said Father. "As the first rays of sun struck Marneen's hut, he opened his eyes. The morning had begun. He dressed quickly. It did not take him very long. He had only one piece of clothing to put on. It was a robe with a hole for the neck and

11

two for his arms. He tied it in the middle with an embroidered girdle. Then he slipped his feet into his sandals and washed his face and hands. His mother gave him his breakfast. She baked pancakes of coarse corn meal and gave them to Marneen with a small clay jug of cool goat's milk. She gave him some cakes and a piece of cheese for his lunch.

"Then Marneen went off with his flock of sheep. He carried a flute too. He called his flute a *chalil*. While the sheep nibbled among the rocks and the grass, he played the flute. He played for fun and because it helped him to take care of his flock. Sometimes a lamb would stray too far. Then Marneen followed him and played a tune. The lamb came back. After a while Marneen felt hungry. He looked up at the sky. Yes, the sun was directly overhead. It was noon, the middle of the day—time for lunch. Marneen ate his cakes and his cheese. He walked over to the little brook. The water ran clear and cool. How good it tasted!

"Marneen felt tired. The sheep were lying down in the shade of the rocks and the bushes. They would be quiet for a while. He looked for a shady spot. He lay down to rest. Far away he could see the little mud brick huts of the village. Here he was all alone. He dozed a little. When he woke up the

shadows were lengthening. The sun was lower in the heavens. It was afternoon. Slowly the sun slipped down in the sky. Marneen knew it was time to collect his sheep. He called to them on the chalil. They came together. In the long shadows of the afternoon sun, Marneen went home with his sheep. The sun disappeared. A day had passed."

"Marneen measured his day by the sun," said Joseph.

"But what about the weeks and the months?" cried Hillel. "How did he count them? Did he have a calendar?"

"That is another story. I will tell it to you to-morrow night. In the meantime, why don't you think about it? Perhaps you will find the answer yourselves."

"Give us a hint," begged Leah.

"All right," said Father. "I will help you. Think about the moon. That will help you to guess how Marneen knew about the months as they passed by."

Thirty Days Hath September

Upstairs in his room, Hillel got ready for bed. He thought about the moon. That was the hint Father had given. It was a riddle. What was the answer?

Perhaps the answer was in his calendar. He took it off the wall and threw himself down on his bed. He looked at the calendar very carefully. Yes, there was a picture of the moon on it. In fact there was more. There were four different pictures of the moon, like this:

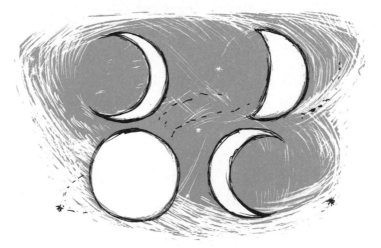

He could close his eyes and see the moon just as it was on the pictures. Sometimes the moon was just a thin curved line. A few nights later it was larger; it became a half-moon. Then it grew bright and full. You could see the man in the moon on those nights. Then once again it changed. It grew thinner and thinner and seemed to disappear.

Was that the answer to the riddle? Hillel was pretty sure he had guessed it. Full moon, half-moon, quarter-moon—Hillel was asleep.

"I think I know the answer to our question," he said, as they all sat around with Mother and Father the next evening. "The calendar told me. During the day Marneen watched the sun. It told him when it was morning, afternoon, and night. At night he followed the moon. He watched it grow. It became larger every night. At last it was full. Then he watched it grow smaller night by night. He counted the time from one full moon to another."

"That is fine," exclaimed Father. "You have made a good guess, Hillel. The moon did tell Marneen and his father about the months and even about the holidays. But they did not have to wait for the full moon. They watched for the new moon. Marneen's father might say to him, 'When another moon has come, it will be time to go to Jerusalem for the sacrifice.' Or he might say, 'When the moon is full, the festival will begin.' "

"Could they always tell when the new moon began to show?" asked Joseph. "Did they watch so carefully?"

"That is a good question," said Father. "Marneen and his father might not always notice the new moon. But in Jerusalem, men were appointed to watch. As soon as the new moon appeared, they ran to tell the judges of the high court. At least two men had to see it. That was to make sure there was no mistake. Then something very exciting happened."

Leah began to jump up and down on the sofa. "What was that? What was that?"

"When the judges were sure the new moon was in the sky, they ordered their officials to light fire signals on the highest hill in Jerusalem. The fire had to be seen for miles around. When the people in other towns and villages saw the signals they knew a new month had begun. They signaled with fires or torches. The Land of Israel was not very large. Soon everyone knew that a new moon had appeared."

"I would like that job," said Hillel. "I would build the biggest bonfire. You could see it all over the country. You would not need any calendar."

17

"What would you do for Jews who lived far away?" said Mother.

The children were quiet. That was a hard question. Suddenly Joseph had an idea. "I would send them a messenger."

Mother and Father laughed together. Joseph was right. "That's exactly what they did. They sent messengers to announce the new moon and the days of the holidays. The messengers traveled on donkeys or on camels. But the messengers were sometimes late. People in far-off lands could not be sure when a holiday began. They thought of something new. They celebrated the holidays for two days. One of them was surely correct."

"I wondered about that," said Joseph.

"Orthodox Jews still celebrate two days of certain important holidays," said Father.

"But now we have calendars," said Hillel. "We do not have to watch for the moon."

"Yes," said Father. "As the years passed by, wise men all over the world were studying the sun, the moon, and the stars. They watched the heavens. They made tables and charts. They wrote down all they learned. At last they figured out a calendar. They learned that it takes about 365 days for the earth to move around the sun. That makes a year—

one year according to the sun. They divided the year into twelve months. You know that."

Leah began to chant, "Thirty days hath September,
April, June, and November,"

The boys joined in, "All the rest have thirty-one,
Excepting February which has twenty-eight,
Rain or shine—
And in a leap year, twenty-nine."

"The calendar for the sun year is the calendar that we use every day. It is the one I have hanging over my desk."

"What about the Hebrew calendar?" asked Hillel.

"Mother told you that the Hebrew calendar is called a luach. It also has twelve months. But they are shorter than the months on our calendar. An exact month has twenty-nine and a half days. That is the time from one new moon to the next."

The children were listening carefully. Joseph began to figure. "Then the Hebrew calendar does not have as many days as our calendar."

"The moon year has only 354 days. It is eleven days shorter than the sun year, because each moon month is only twenty-nine and a half days long."

Joseph spoke slowly. He was thinking hard. "Something has to be done," he said. "The luach cannot be correct. If it loses eleven days every year, the holidays will soon get mixed up. My goodness, we will be celebrating Pesach in the wintertime before long."

"Long, long ago, the wise men thought of that. They learned how to keep the Hebrew calendar in order. Every two or three years becomes a leap year."

"They add an extra day," Leah cried out.

"No, Leah," said Father, "an extra day would not help very much. We need many more days. When the leap year comes, a whole month is added. That keeps the moon calendar in order. The holidays are celebrated at the right season. Passover always comes in the springtime, and Sukos always comes in the fall."

"We do not have to worry about the calendar any more," said Mother. "It is set for years and years and years." She went over to the desk. "Would you like to see the luach?" she asked.

The children watched as Mother opened the

20

little book. "It begins with Rosh Ha-shono," she said. "It shows on what days of the English calendar the holiday will fall. Then it goes on month after month. The dates of all the holidays are shown."

"The luach shows everything," cried Hillel. "It is a double calendar. It is an English calendar, and a Hebrew calendar. It shows the American holidays and the Jewish holidays. Here they are—Columbus Day, Thanksgiving Day, Chanuko, New Year's Day, Tu Bi-Sh'vot—" He stopped to catch his breath.

"Yes, they are all here," Mother agreed.

"We have learned a lot tonight," said Joseph. "But there's one thing you didn't explain, Daddy. You said that the Orthodox Jews still celebrate some holidays for two days. What about the Reform Jews? When did they decide to celebrate those holidays for only one day?"

"It is more than a hundred years since Reform Jews began to think about this question. Now that we have a correct calendar, we know exactly when each holiday begins. The rabbis thought about it long and carefully. They knew that the Bible tells us to keep the holidays for just one day. And they knew that the Jews living in the Land of Israel celebrate for only one day. So you see there were many good reasons for deciding to celebrate the holidays for one day instead of two."

"I would like to have a luach," said Hillel. "Let us each have a luach to put right next to our calendars."

"That's easy," said Mother. "Some day next week we will get a luach for each one of you."

A Visit to a Jewish Bookstore

School was over. Hillel rushed out. He ran down the wide front steps of the school building. He carried his school bag. It was heavy with books and notebooks.

"Hillel," someone called.

Hillel looked up. He was surprised. Mother was waiting for him in their automobile. Hillel ran over to her.

"Would you like to go downtown with me to buy a luach?" asked Mother.

"Oh, yes," answered Hillel. "Are Joseph and Leah coming, too?"

"No," said Mother. "Joseph is staying at school for his singing group, and Leah has a little cold. She did not go back to her class this afternoon. Come on, hop in."

Hillel jumped in beside Mother. "Where are we going?" he asked.

"Downtown on 4th Street there is a Jewish bookstore. It has many things besides books. We can buy our luachs there. Or, we can go to the tem-

ple. They may have some luachs in the gift shop."
Mother stopped to think. "No, we'll go downtown.
I did not see any luachs in the temple gift shop."

Hillel liked to go downtown. He did not go very
often. Usually there was a good reason for the trip.
When he needed new shoes or a new suit, he went
to the downtown shops. Sometimes Mother took
him along when she called for Father at his office.

Very soon Mother said, "Here is the store."
They got out of the car. They stood in front of the
store and looked in the window.

"Look, Mother," Hillel cried. He pointed to a
book in the window. "We have that book." It was
one of Leah's books, called *Purim Parade*. "Let's go
in."

They opened the door. A short dark man came
up to them. "Good afternoon," he said. "I am Mr.
Levine. Can I help you?"

"Yes," said Mother. "We would like to buy a
luach for Hillel and a luach for Joseph and one for
Leah. They each want a luach."

"You can have your choice," said Mr. Levine.
"I have many different kinds. Here are a few you
can look at."

He placed three small booklets on the table.
Hillel looked at them. They each showed the Eng-

lish months and the Hebrew months. It was hard to decide. One of them had many colored pictures. "Let us take this one," said Hillel. "It has a picture for every month. I like it."

"That is a good choice," said Mr. Levine. "That luach comes from the State of Israel. It is a children's luach."

"Now may I look around?" asked Hillel. "I have never been in a store like this before."

Mr. Levine laughed. "Of course," he said. "Ask me about anything you don't understand."

First Hillel looked in the showcases. He saw a talis with long fringes and blue stripes. He knew that a talis is a prayer-shawl. Father had one. He wore it when he went to the Conservative synagogue with Uncle Lou. In the synagogue every man wore such a prayer-shawl. In the temple where Hillel went with his family, the rabbi wore a talis over his black gown.

In the same showcase lay something that Hillel had never seen before. It was a pair of small leather cases. "What are these?" asked Hillel.

"Those are *t'filin*," said Mr. Levine. He opened the showcase and took them out. Attached to each box was a long leather strap. "There are verses from the Torah in Hebrew written on a piece of parch-

ment inside each box. Orthodox Jews put them on every morning when they say their prayers, except on Shabos. One little box is placed on the forehead, and one is placed on the left arm. The leather straps are wound about the head and around the left arm."

"Is there a reason for that?" asked Hillel.

"The rabbis say that when a man wears t'filin he will worship God with his head and with his heart. So we use the left arm which is near the heart. Wearing t'filin is a very old custom among Jews."

Everywhere that Hillel looked there was something to see. From Israel there was a china Passover plate. Near it stood a brass Chanuko Menorah and next to that was a pair of candlesticks, like Mother lit on Friday evenings.

There were many other things that Hillel saw. He was surprised at how many he recognized. In one case lay a shofor. Around it were many Rosh

Ha-shono cards. There were book ends with Hebrew letters and a desk set from the State of Israel.

And books, and books, and books! Hebrew books and English books. Prayer books and history books. Story books and picture books.

"There is a Jewish book to suit everyone here," said Hillel. "One for you, Mother, and one for Father, and one for every child."

"Yes," said Mr. Levine. He picked up a book. "Here is a new book written by a rabbi. That would suit your father. Perhaps your mother would like the Jewish cook book. And your brother could read this history book. What would you choose for yourself?"

"I would take this story book," said Hillel. "And I would get the picture book for Leah. But I must wait until I have more money for all those books. I used up my money for Chanuko. Now I must start saving again."

On the walls hung many pictures. Mr. Levine saw that Hillel was looking at them carefully. "Some of the most famous artists in the world have painted pictures about the Bible and about Jewish heroes," he said. "These are copies of some well-known paintings. If you visit the Museum of Art, you may see some of the originals."

"Have you seen enough?" Mother asked. "Now we must call for Father. But we will come again."

Mr. Levine gave Mother three packages. Mother marked them on the outside, Joseph, Hillel, Leah. Each child would open a package and find his own luach.

Mr. Levine walked to the door with them. "Come to see us again," he said.

Hillel had an idea. He would speak to Joseph and Leah. The next time they wanted to give Mother or Father a present, they would go to the Jewish bookstore and pick out a book or a picture.

"Thank you," he said. "We'll come again."

Four New Years

Mother and Father, Joseph, Hillel, and Leah were walking home from the temple. It was a cool September evening. The stars were very bright. The moon was only a thin line in the sky.

"Look at the moon," said Hillel. "It is just a thin line. I know why."

"I know why, too," said Joseph.

Leah kept quiet. She wished she knew why, too. For a moment she pretended she knew as much as her brothers. But she was curious. She could not help herself. She had to ask. "Why, why?" she cried. "Please tell me."

"Because this is Rosh Ha-shono. And it's the first evening of the month. So, of course, the moon is just coming out. Don't you remember how Daddy explained it to us?" asked Hillel.

"I do remember now. We found out about the moon from our Hebrew calendars." Leah was sad. Why did she have to forget?

Father asked a question. "Which New Year comes out on the fifteenth day of the month?"

30

Hillel and Joseph looked at each other. They were surprised. A New Year on the fifteenth day of the month?

"You should know," Father teased. "You celebrate it each year."

Leah cried out, "You forgot, too." Now she felt better. She wasn't the only one to forget.

By now the family was home. They walked up the steps of the house and went in. How cheerful and bright it was. The rooms were full of flowers. The Rosh Ha-shono candles still shone. Mother had blessed very tall candles that evening and they burned for many hours. Next to them on the table were a beautiful rosy apple and a small jar of honey. A carafe of red wine stood nearby, sparkling in the candlelight. Anyone who came in would know that the holiday of Rosh Ha-shono was being celebrated.

"Please tell us, Daddy," Joseph asked, as they walked into the house.

"It's very late," said Mother. "And we are all going to temple services in the morning." Even Leah was going along to the children's service.

"Let us sit together for just a few moments," said Father.

Hillel and Joseph threw themselves down on the floor. They enjoyed looking up at Father. Leah sat

on a low stool. "Now tell us about the New Year that comes on the 15th of the month," she said.

"It's the New Year for Trees," was Father's reply.

"Tu Bi-Sh'vot," called Hillel and Joseph together.

"Yes, Tu Bi-Sh'vot or Chamisho Osor Bi-Sh'vot means the fifteenth day of the month of Sh'vot. That's when we celebrate the New Year for Trees." Hillel and Joseph looked at each other. Of course! They remembered very well.

"There are two more New Years in the Jewish year," Father went on. But Mother interrupted him. She came in with a tray. On the tray were glasses of milk and cookies and slices of honey cake.

"If you are staying up," she said, "you may have some milk and cake."

The children were happy. It was getting to be a sort of party.

"Please go on," Hillel begged. He had a white mustache on his lips from the milk. His voice was husky, because his mouth was almost full of cake. But Father understood him.

"The holiday we are celebrating tonight is the first day of the month of Tishri. According to our luach, Tishri is the first month of the year. But the

Bible calls it the seventh month. We are not sure how this difference came about, as this all goes back thousands of years. And of course, it doesn't really matter now."

"If this is the seventh month," asked Hillel, "what does the Bible call the first month?"

"It is the month of Nison," answered Father. "It comes in the Spring."

"That is the month of Pesach," said Joseph. He spoke clearly. He had finished his milk and cake.

"You are right," said Father. "Passover is celebrated on the evening of the fifteenth day of Nison. And the first day of Nison was a New Year's Day, too. It was called the King's New Year."

"A special New Year for the king," Leah said, softly.

"There was a special reason for it," Father explained. "It kept track of how long the king was ruling. Let's suppose the king began to reign two weeks before the first of Nison. Two weeks later, the New Year for Kings came around. Then the king's chamberlain would say, 'The king has been on the throne for one year.' But if he became king two weeks *after* the first of Nison, the king's year was not finished until the first of Nison came around almost a year later."

34

"Did anyone else pay attention to the King's New Year?" Hillel wanted to know.

"I'll ask you a question. When you write a letter how do you begin?"

"I write the date across the top of the letter," answered Hillel.

"In ancient days, most people could not write. There were special men called scribes who wrote letters and important papers for them. When a scribe wrote a letter he began it like this: 'In the third year of the reign of King David, or King Josiah or King Uzziah.' The men who wrote the Bible used the King's New Year all the time."

"Are there any more New Years?" asked Leah. "So far we have a New Year for the people, a New Year for trees, and a New Year for the king."

"I hope there are no more," said Mother. "We must go to bed."

"But there is another—just one more."

"Another New Year!" Even Mother was surprised.

"Yes. This New Year takes place on the first day of Elul, just one month before our New Year on the first of Tishri."

"Whom is it for?" asked Mother. She forgot about sending the children to bed.

"It's a New Year for cattle, for cows and sheep."

"How did they celebrate?" asked Hillel. "Did they get special grass to eat?"

"Perhaps they did. In ancient times, a man gave a present to the Temple in Jerusalem every year. He gave one-tenth of all he had. A rich man could give gold and silver. A shepherd could give sheep or cattle. A farmer could bring bags of wheat. But no matter what else they gave, nearly everyone brought a fine animal to the Temple as a sacrifice to God. On the first of Elul, the cattle for the Temple were chosen."

"Do people do that now?" asked Hillel.

"No," said Father. "We give money to our temples and synagogues, to hospitals and to schools. We help people in need in our own country and in lands far away. A man who gives part of what he earns every year to charity is following an ancient custom. It goes all the way back to Bible times."

Suddenly Mother stood up. "To bed, everyone," she cried. "You can dream about all the New Years—for people and for kings, for cattle and for trees. No one and no thing has been forgotten."

A Good Deed

Leah sat with Joseph on a bench in the park, only a block away from the temple. They were waiting for Hillel.

It was late afternoon. The sun was making its way westward across the sky. The shadows of the trees were long and thin.

"Yom Kippur is a long day," said Leah.

"That is because it is a day for thinking instead of a day for doing," Joseph answered.

Leah added, "It is a day for praying. I found that out today when I went with you and Hillel to the children's services this morning." She looked around. "I wish Hillel would come. Then we can go into the big temple to sit with Mother and Daddy for the last part of the service. That's the part of Yom Kippur I like the best."

But where was Hillel? Joseph looked at his watch. Father had lent it to him so the children would come to temple on time. There was still a little while.

"Do you know what Miss Berger told us about Yom Kippur?" he asked. "It is a sort of story."

Leah was always ready to hear a story. Joseph began:

"Long ago people imagined that there were gates in Heaven and that all during Yom Kippur the gates were open. Every prayer could rise up and enter the gates. Then as the day was over, the gates of heaven slowly closed. Yom Kippur prayers were finished. It was time to go home. Everyone hoped for a happy year to come."

"There is something I don't understand," said Leah. "On Yom Kippur people are sorry for wrong things they did during the year. The temple is full. I don't think all those men and women need to be forgiven."

"Most people come to thank God for all the good things that happened during the year. But sometimes—Leah, I have to ask you a question. Do you remember your birthday party?"

Of course Leah remembered her birthday party. She had a wonderful time. Mother baked a birthday cake. All her friends came to the party. No—not all her friends. One of them was left out.

"What happened to Jenny?" asked Joseph.

Leah looked sad. "I forgot to invite her," she

38

answered. "She was unhappy. I told her I was sorry."

"There you are," declared Joseph. "You didn't mean to hurt Jenny's feelings. You forgot. Grownups forget too. They make mistakes. They are sorry too. Even very good people can sometimes make mistakes. On Yom Kippur everyone has a whole day for thinking things over. They make up their minds to do better next year."

Leah was anxious to get to temple. She looked up at the sky. "The sun is getting lower."

"It must be almost time for the closing prayers. What shall we do about Hillel?"

Joseph and Leah got up from the bench. They walked out of the park. They stood at the entrance. Leah looked one way. Joseph looked the other. They could not see Hillel.

Leah said, "Here is Daddy."

Father was coming across the street. He joined them. "I came for you," he said. "There is room for you to sit with Mother and me. Our family can pray together as Yom Kippur ends."

"But Hillel isn't here. What shall we do?" Leah was ready to cry.

Father looked both ways. "Wait a minute," he said. "Someone is running."

Yes, it was Hillel. He was running toward

them. He reached them. He was all out of breath.

"Come and sit down for a minute," said Father. He led them to a bench. "Catch your breath. Then tell us why you are so late."

Hillel took a deep breath. "I took a walk after the children's service. I met Cousin David. We walked up to school and then we turned back. It took longer than we thought. We began to hurry. Then something happened."

"What was it?" Leah was impatient.

"We came to a small house. It was on a hill. A baby carriage was standing outside. Just before we reached it, the carriage began to roll down the hill. We ran after it. It rolled very fast. But David ran faster. He got ahead of it. He caught it just as it reached the bottom of the hill. I grabbed the handles. We stopped the carriage."

"Was there a baby in it?" asked Father.

"Yes," Hillel answered. "And the baby began to cry. He cried and cried. We were frightened. We wheeled the carriage back up the hill."

"Go on," said Father. "Tell us the rest."

"I walked up to the house and rang the bell. A lady came out. I told her what had happened. She ran out and picked up the baby. She was frightened, too. The baby stopped crying. The lady thanked us.

She wanted to give us a present. But we didn't take it. We hurried away. David went to the synagogue and I came here."

Father smiled. "You are not the first one who stopped to do a good deed on his way to the synagogue. There is an old story about a rabbi who came late to the synagogue on Yom Kippur Eve for Kol Nidrei. Everyone was asking, 'Where is the rabbi?' At last he arrived. He explained. 'On my way to the synagogue I heard a baby crying. I went into the house. The baby was alone. I held the baby until it went to sleep. It did not matter if I came a little late to the services. It was important to help the baby. A good deed always comes first.' "

Leah was very pleased. She was proud of Hillel and of Cousin David. They had done a good deed on Yom Kippur.

The children crossed over the street with Father. They walked down the wide center aisle of the temple. Mother was waiting for them. She had seats for them. The family sat together. The temple became quiet. The closing services began.

Mother and Father were reading softly from their prayer books. Joseph and Hillel read too. Leah listened quietly. She heard the low hum of many voices. She thought, "Perhaps there are gates of

heaven. If so, they are open for my prayers, too."
She prayed, "Please God, let me be good this year.
I don't want to make mistakes again. I don't want
to hurt Jenny's feelings again. Help me to be good."

Leah's sweet voice joined the voices of all the
people in the temple. Her prayer became a part of
their prayers.

Through the windows, the sun was going lower
and lower. The shofor was blown. The last "Amen"
was said. The long Yom Kippur Day, the day of
fasting and thinking and praying, came to an end.

The "Almost-Suko"

The front door opened with a bang. "Come and see what we have," Hillel called. Mother and Leah were upstairs. They ran down.

Father, Joseph, and Hillel stood in the hall. Next to them was a large basket. It was filled with evergreen boughs. In their hands Hillel and Joseph were holding bunches of cornstalks.

"We were helping to decorate two temple sukos," said Joseph. "One is inside on the pulpit. The other is outside on the lawn. We covered them with green branches like these from pine and fir trees. They are beautiful. The temple sukos are ready for the holiday. There were lots of branches left over. We brought some of them home."

"What shall we do with them?" asked Mother.

Father explained. "We thought we could decorate the dining-room to look something like a suko."

Leah picked up an armful of branches. She was ready to begin.

"Is there time?" asked Mother. "The holiday will begin very soon. We are having guests for dinner. And then we will all go to temple. We must be clean and dressed for Sukos."

"We will hurry. We will all help," cried the children.

Mother agreed. Everyone went to work. Father got a tall step-ladder. He hung green branches from the chandelier. Hillel and Joseph tucked greens behind the pictures on the walls. They tied up the cornstalks and stood them up in the corners of the room.

Mother prepared the table. She put a white tablecloth over it. She let Leah strew some small green twigs over the table. In the center Mother heaped high a mound of fruits and vegetables. Orange carrots with long green leaves, and red and green peppers made a border; purple and yellow grapes, criss-crossed apples, pears and plums in the middle.

Father turned to Hillel. "Now get the *esrog* and the *lulov*," he said. Hillel ran into the study. He was happy to get them. He had gone with Father to the Jewish Bookstore to buy them. He laid them on the table next to Father's place, near the *chalo* and the wine, waiting for the holiday blessing.

There was still work to do. Hillel and Joseph swept up the pine needles and leaves which had

fallen on the floor. Father put away the ladder. Mother placed her bright candlesticks on the table, and Leah carried in the candles. Then they stood for a moment and looked at what they had done.

"It is an almost-suko," said Leah.

"Yes," said Father. "Most sukos are built out-of-doors. Through their green roofs you can see the stars twinkling in the sky. But I like our suko very much. We have done a good job."

"I think we have everything here to remind us of Sukos," said Joseph. "The fruits and vegetables show that it is a harvest festival. Besides, we have the esrog and the lulov."

Leah broke in. "And our almost-suko reminds us of the times the Hebrews lived in booths. We made booths in our class. That's how I know."

Hillel felt strange. He was happy and a little sad at the same time. "If we could only see the stars," he said to Father.

"When it is dark," said Father, "we will be walking to the temple for services. We will see the stars in the sky. We will see what a great and wonderful world we live in."

"Now let us go up to our rooms and get ready for the holiday," said Mother. "Our guests will be here soon."

47

The guests were Stanley and his parents. But Stanley couldn't wait. He came early. Hillel was clean and dressed in his new suit. When Stanley rang the bell, Hillel opened the door. He took him right into the dining-room. Stanley stared at the room and its decorations.

"It is just like a suko," he said.

"We have an almost-suko," Hillel answered. "All we need is an open roof and the stars shining through. But we do have everything else."

"My father has stars," said Stanley.

Hillel began to laugh. What could Stanley mean?

"Your father has stars!" he repeated.

"Yes, and I'll go for them." Without another word, Stanley dashed out of the house. Hillel waited. Stanley's house was so near, he would be back soon.

He was back in a few minutes. His father came, too. Mr. Stern was carrying a box. Hillel called, "Daddy, please come downstairs."

Father came down. Mr. Stern explained. "The high school had a play. I helped them. We had a make-believe sky. We had an electric moon and stars to match it. I brought over the stars for you."

Father and Mr. Stern strung the stars across

48

the ceiling. They hid them among the green boughs.
It did not take long.

Mr. Stern pushed the switch. The stars lit up.
They twinkled. He turned them off. "We will have
them later," he said.

Mother came in with the other children. Mrs.
Stern arrived, too.

"May we begin?" asked Mother.

"Yes," Father answered. "We are ready to celebrate Sukos."

Mother lit the candles. She recited the holiday
blessing over them. She added the special blessing,
*Boruch ato Adonoi Elohenu melech ho-olom, she-
he-che-yonu, v'ki-monu, v'hi-gi-onu, laz'man ha-ze*—
"Praised be Thou, O Lord, our God, who hast permitted us to be present at this happy time." Then
everyone said, "Amen," and sat down at the table.
Father lifted the cup of wine and said the blessings.
Joseph said the blessing for the bread. Everyone
said, "Amen."

"There ought to be a special blessing for the suko," said Stanley.

"Oh, there is one," Father explained, "but we will have to wait to say it."

"Why?" the children wanted to know.

"The blessing is called, 'to sit in the suko.' We ought to be in a real suko to say it. When we visit the temple suko, we can say it there. I will teach it to you."

"Ours is only an almost-suko," said Leah. "But we have nearly everything—everything but the stars shining through the roof." She stopped short. There *were* stars. She could see them twinkling over her head. Hillel had turned on the switch.

That was fun! Father explained. The family and their holiday guests sat around happily. The fresh smell of the evergreen twigs filled the room. The holiday candles shone.

Sukos in the almost-suko was very good.

From Year to Year

There were two more days to Sukos week, but the "almost-suko" was gone. It had lasted from Sunday until Friday. Then it began to look shabby. Pine needles were on the floor. Some of the branches were bare. On Friday afternoon Hillel and Joseph came home from school. They took down all the twigs and branches. They saved the esrog and the lulov to decorate the table for Shabos. Joseph stood on the ladder and carefully removed the stars. Hillel carried them over to Stanley's house. He thanked Mrs. Stern for the stars.

On the way home, Hillel saw Father get out of his car in front of the house. He was not alone. Another man was with him. The man was carrying a suitcase. Hillel ran to meet them.

"Hello, Hillel," said Father. "This is my friend, Mr. Miller. We have been friends for many years, since we were boys like you and Joseph. Mr. Miller will stay with us until Simchas Torah—the last day of Sukos."

They walked up the steps and into the house.

Mother said, "Welcome," to Mr. Miller. Joseph and Leah were with her.

"Take Mr. Miller to his room upstairs," said Mother to Joseph.

"May all the children come?" asked the guest. "I have a gift for them."

"We will all go with you," said Father. But Mother stayed behind. She was fixing the good Sabbath dinner.

In the guest room, Mr. Miller opened his suitcase. He took out a long box and gave it to Joseph.

"Open the box, Joseph," he said.

The children crowded around. Joseph opened the box. It was lined with red silk. On the silk lining lay a small Torah. The Torah had a red velvet cover, like the big ones in the Ark in the temple.

"On Sunday night," said Mr. Miller, "I suppose we will go to temple to celebrate Simchas Torah. The men will carry the large Torahs around the temple. I thought you would like to have a Torah of your own to carry. You can each take a turn going around the temple with it."

"A Torah of our own!" The children were excited.

"This is not a real Torah," Father explained. "This is a printed copy. The Torahs in the synagogue

are written by hand. They are made of parchment. Parchment is the skin of an animal. It has been cleaned and dried and stretched and made ready for writing. It lasts for years and years and years."

"All written by hand," Joseph repeated. "What a job. It must take very long."

"It does," said Mr. Miller. "My father was a writer of Torahs. He knew the Torah very well. He knew Hebrew very well. Besides, he was a good and pious man. He was called a scribe. The Hebrew name for that is a *Sofer*."

"I remember," said Father. "Sometimes if we were very quiet, he would let us watch him."

"He had special, pure black ink for his writing."

"And he didn't use a pen. He used a goose quill. It had a feather on the end."

Father and Mr. Miller looked at each other and laughed. They were remembering the days when they were boys.

"Now may we see our Torah?" asked Joseph.

"Of course," said Mr. Miller. He took off the velvet cover. Underneath it, the Torah was rolled up on two wooden rods with handles. It was tied together with a red satin ribbon.

"Untie the ribbon, Leah," said Father. Leah untied the red bow with her little fingers.

Mr. Miller picked up the small Torah and laid
it on the desk in the room. He unrolled it, until it
was at the very beginning of the Bible. The right
roll was thin. The left roll was fat.

"I know the Hebrew letters," said Joseph. "But
I cannot read the words."

"That is because the Torah is written without
vowels. It has no little dots under the letters. I will
read the first sentence for you." He read. *B'reshis
boro Elohim es ha-shomayim v'es ho-oretz.* Then
he translated, "In the beginning, God created the
heavens and the earth."

"In the beginning—" Hillel repeated. "Long,
long ago. Just like a story."

"How does it end?" asked Joseph.

"I will roll the Torah to the end. Then we will see." Mr. Miller rolled the Torah to the end. Now the right roll was fat. The left roll was thin. Mr. Miller read the Hebrew to himself. Then he translated it into English. "And since that time, there has not been in Israel a prophet like Moses, who did all the wonders which God sent him to do.

"Let me tell you a little about the Torah. It is divided into five books. They are the first five books of the Bible. They are called the Five Books of Moses. They begin with the story of how God created the world. They end with the story of Moses and how he died."

The children were silent for a moment. They thought about Moses. They knew many stories about him.

"What part of the Torah will be read on Simchas Torah in the temple?" asked Joseph.

"Have you been to the temple on Shabos?" asked Mr. Miller.

The children nodded their heads.

"Then you have seen the rabbi read from the Torah Scroll. He reads a portion each week. Now I will tell you something important. On Simchas Torah he comes to the end of the Five Books of

Moses. He reads the last few verses in the scroll. And then—" Mr. Miller paused.

"And then—" Leah repeated.

"And then, the rabbi turns to another Torah Scroll. This one has been rolled to the very beginning. The rabbi reads the first words of the Five Books of Moses, 'In the beginning God created the heavens and the earth.'"

"The end and the beginning," said Hillel.

"Yes," said Mr. Miller. "It takes a whole year to read the entire Torah week by week. It takes from one Simchas Torah to the next Simchas Torah to read the whole scroll. But we never really finish with the Five Books of Moses or with the whole Bible. We always begin again."

"Tell us some more about your father and how he wrote a Torah," asked Joseph.

"When my father wrote a Torah," Mr. Miller went on, "he wrote every letter and every line very carefully. They had to be exactly right. There could not be a mistake. But when he came to the last page, he wrote some of the letters in very lightly. He would just write an outline of the letters."

The children wondered why. "After the Torah was brought to the synagogue, he would finish those

57

letters. A man would say, 'I have a new grandson. His name is Samuel. His name begins with a *Shin*,' like this." Mr. Miller wrote the Hebrew letter shin.

" 'Please find a shin for my grandson,' the man would say. My father would look for a word with a shin in it. He would fill in the letter. Little Samuel had his own letter in the Torah. The man would give some money to the synagogue. After a while all the letters were filled in. The synagogue received many presents. Everyone was happy. The day that a Torah was completed was a holiday. There was a celebration in the synagogue."

Leah could hardly wait to ask. "Is the letter of my name in the Torah?" she cried.

"And mine?" asked Joseph.

"And mine?" asked Hillel.

"Let's take a look," said Mr. Miller. He rolled the Torah back again. "Here we are," he cried. "At the very beginning. The third word is *Elohim*, the name of God. The first letter of each of your names is found in that word. There is a *Yod* for Yosef or Joseph. There is *Hay* for Hillel, and a *Lamed* for Leah." He wrote them all down like this.

        י   Yosef—Joseph
       ה   Hillel—Hillel
       ל   Le-ah—Leah

Then he wrote אלהים. "You can see the letters of your names," he said.

Joseph and Hillel rolled the Torah up again. Both sides of the scroll were equal. Leah tied the ribbon on again. She put the velvet cover on the Torah. She placed it carefully in the box.

"Let's take turns keeping the Torah," said Joseph. "Leah, you may have it first. Then Hillel and I will take a turn, too."

"Simchas Torah means Rejoicing in the Torah— being happy that we have the Bible and all it teaches us," said Father. He turned to Mr. Miller. "You have made us all very happy with the wonderful present you brought us. It will bring us joy many times, not just today."

The Young Lions

Hillel belonged to a boys' club. The club had ten members. It had a Hebrew name—the *K'firim*. Hillel liked the name very much. It meant the young lions.

Jerry was the president of the K'firim. He said, "If the lion is the king of the beasts, I am sure he is brave and also wise. Let that be our motto, 'We will be brave and wise.'"

The K'firim met once a week. Once a month they had a party. It was not hard to find a reason for a party. Sometimes one of the boys had a birthday. Often there was a holiday to celebrate. Each member took a turn to have a meeting or a party at his home.

One afternoon Hillel came home from a meeting. He was excited. He had something important to tell.

"It is my turn to have the next meeting of the K'firim," he told the family. "We are going to celebrate Columbus Day. I would like to have a very nice party."

"If you tell me what to do," said Mother, "I will try to help you."

"I would like to have something special for our meeting," said Hillel, "something different."

"It should be a Jewish party because K'firim is a club of Jewish boys," said Leah.

"But Columbus Day is an American holiday," said Joseph, "and all the boys are Americans."

"We are all Jews and Americans," said Hillel.

"Do you know that there were Jews who helped Columbus? Some even came over with him," said Joseph.

"Are you sure?" Hillel was surprised.

"Yes," said Joseph. "I will show you where I read that in my history book."

Sure enough, there it was. "Before Columbus left Spain, he went to a map-maker. The map-maker was named Abraham Zacuto. He was a Jew. Columbus used Zacuto's tables and charts to help him on his journey."

"Did he have a map of America?" asked Leah.

Everyone laughed. "Nobody knew about America then," said Joseph. "It was waiting for Columbus and his men to find it."

"Did the map-maker go along with Columbus?" asked Leah.

"No. But the ship's doctor came from a Jewish family. His name was Bernal."

Mother also read the page in the history book. Then she said, "I want to tell you something that is not written in your book. Try to imagine what it was like when Columbus reached the shores of America. It was early in the morning when land was sighted. Seventy days had passed—seventy days of sailing on the great ocean. How happy the men were. They were safe. They had crossed the unknown sea."

"They must have been brave," said Hillel. "Columbus could have joined our club. He was brave and wise."

Mother went on. "At last they stepped off the boats. The very first man to step on the shores of the New World was Luis de Torres, who also came from a Jewish family. He was the interpreter. He was the first because he hoped he would be able to talk to the people they were to meet. Luis de Torres knew Spanish, Hebrew, and Arabic. But the Indians did not know any of these languages. Luis de Torres could not talk to them at first. But he must have made friends with them for later on he settled down in Cuba and lived there for many years."

"My book says that no one knows for sure if Columbus was a Jew, but some people think he was," said Joseph.

"He had many Jewish friends, and Jews in Spain gave him great sums of money. One of these men was Luis de Santangel, a friend and adviser of the king. Queen Isabella and King Ferdinand did not have enough money for Columbus. Luis de Santangel added money of his own and Columbus was able to buy his ships and fit them out. The first letter Columbus wrote from the New World telling of his discovery went to Luis de Santangel."

"You have all helped me," said Hillel. "I have an idea. I know how to have a good Columbus Day meeting for the K'firim."

63

The Party

Every afternoon after school Hillel went down to the playroom in the basement. The first day he just looked around. He was making his plans. After that, he began to move the furniture around. Then he came upstairs. He asked Mother's advice. He went to the stationery store. He came home with packages and took them downstairs.

At last Columbus Day arrived. The boys came early in the afternoon. Hillel took them to the playroom. What did they see?

The room was decorated like a ship. On the wall hung a large map of the world. But it was not like a map of the world which is seen today. It was very strange. Only Europe and parts of Asia and Africa were shown on the map. Letters were printed where North and South America should have been. The printing said, "The Unknown Seas." In the middle of "The Unknown Seas" was a large X. Next to the X were small letters. They said, "Where Columbus landed—America."

The boys came into the room on a gangplank.

As they entered, Hillel gave each one a sailor's hat.

"This is a new game," said Hillel. "I made it up. It is like 'Pin the Tail on the Donkey.' Whoever comes nearest to America wins a prize."

Each of the boys received a tiny ship with a pin. One by one the boys were blindfolded. Then they tried to find America. Some of the little ships landed in Europe and Africa. Some came very near to America. Jerry came the nearest. He won the prize. It was a "Do it yourself kit," for a small sailboat.

There were other games and prizes. Then Jerry called the meeting to order. Cousin David was the secretary. He read the minutes. Stanley was the treasurer. He collected five cents from every member. He added up his account. "We have three dollars and fifty cents in our treasury," he announced.

The boys were pleased. They had many ideas about the money in their treasury. Some boys wanted to have a movie party. Some boys thought the money should go to charity. Some boys wanted to send the money to the State of Israel. "Let us wait until the end of the year. Then we will decide what to do with our treasury," said Stanley.

Cousin David had something to say. "I have a letter to read. It is from the State of Israel. It is from a boys' club in Haifa. They want some pen pals. Should we be their pen pals?"

The members of the K'firim had to decide what to do. Each one had something to say. Most of them thought it would be fun to write to boys in Haifa. "Must we write in Hebrew?" asked Hillel. "What shall we do?"

"We can write in English," said David. "When we know enough Hebrew, we can write in Hebrew, too."

The boys took a vote. They decided to write one letter to the club in Haifa. Each member would sign his name. The president picked out Sidney to write the letter. He was the oldest boy in the club.

"Now Hillel has a report to make," said Jerry.

Hillel stood up. He told the boys all he had learned about Columbus and about the Jews who had helped him. It sounded very interesting. The boys were quiet while they listened. When he finished, he said, "Now it is time for refreshments. I will tell Mother we are ready."

The boys pushed the table into the center of the room. It was set with plates and spoons and napkins. They carried their chairs to the table.

Mother came in with a large box. She placed it in the middle of the table. It was tied with a yellow string. "Pull the string, Jerry," she said. "You are the president."

Jerry pulled the string. The sides of the box fell apart.

Inside the box was a large cake. It was decorated with a sugar ship. The name of the ship was written on the side in blue sugar, "The Nina." On the ship were tiny sailors.

"Here is Columbus' ship," said Mother, "together with his sailors. Every member may take home one of the sailors as a souvenir."

Of course, there was ice cream and candy besides the cake. The boys ate and ate. Then it was time to go home.

"I'm glad Columbus discovered America," said David. "This was the best meeting we had."

Hillel was happy. He went up to his room and picked up his calendar. Columbus Day was marked in red because it was a holiday. Now he knew what people meant when they said, "a red-letter day."

Pilgrims

Hillel was cross. What a way to spend Thanksgiving Day—alone, in bed. Of course he wasn't quite alone. Susan, the sitter, was with him. But Mother, Father, Joseph, and Leah were away. They had all gone to Uncle Joe's for Thanksgiving dinner. Hillel knew what they would have, too. He had had Thanksgiving dinner there many times. There would be a big turkey—bigger each year, it seemed to him. And with it, cranberry sauce and stuffing, and yams and pecan pie for dessert. After dinner, the cousins had time to play together. He stopped thinking about all that he was missing and called, "Susie."

Susan was a high school girl who lived nearby. She was the sitter when Mother and Father went out. Joseph and Hillel didn't think they needed a sitter. Mother agreed with them. She had Susan come in to be with Leah. And today, Susan had come only to keep Hillel company for a few hours.

"What is it, Hillel?" asked Susan. She was in Joseph's room looking at a book. She came into Hillel's room. "How do you feel?"

"I'm not happy," Hillel answered. "I don't think I have anything to be thankful for. Why should I get a sore throat just for Thanksgiving Day?"

"Maybe it's because you didn't wear your rubbers when it rained," said Susan.

"How do you know?" cried Hillel. "I was late for school and couldn't stop for rubbers."

"Yes, and you wore wet shoes all morning," said Susan. "I know. It happened to me once, too. I tell you what. Let's play a game. We'll each write down all we know about the people who celebrated the first Thanksgiving Day. Then we'll see who has a better list."

"Do you mean the Pilgrims?" asked Hillel.

Susan nodded. She gave Hillel a pencil and a sheet of paper. She pushed his pillow up behind his back. She brought him a glass of fresh orange juice. He began to feel comfortable. He started to write.

Susan sat on a chair near the bed. She leaned on a book. She was writing, too. The room became silent. Only the sound of two pencils covering two sheets of paper could be heard.

"Done!" cried Hillel. "I wrote six sentences. Each one tells something about Thanksgiving Day."

"Fine," said Susan cheerfully. "Read yours off first. Then I'll read mine."

70

Hillel read:

"The Pilgrims celebrated the first Thanksgiving Day.

"They celebrated it the second year they lived in their new home in America.

"They thanked God that they had a great harvest and that they would have enough to eat during the winter.

"They were thankful because they had friends among some of the Indians.

"They were thankful because they were living in strong log cabins.

"Thanksgiving is called a Harvest Festival."

Hillel finished reading. "Now it is your turn," he said.

Susan began to read. "I am writing about Hebrew Pilgrims. They celebrated their Thanksgiving almost three thousand years ago. They called it the holiday of Sukos. Sukos is a harvest festival. The Hebrews were happy in their home in the land of Palestine. They were thankful for the good harvest of grapes and fruits and grain. For seven days they lived in little booths or sukos to remind them of their days of wandering after they left Egypt. The Bible tells about the harvest festivals of the Hebrews.

"The Pilgrims in America loved the Bible and

71

read it often. That is one reason why they decided to have a harvest festival and thank God for helping them in their new home. They called their festival, Thanksgiving Day."

Susan finished reading. Hillel's eyes were wide open.

"Did the Pilgrims know about the Hebrews?" he asked.

"Yes," answered Susan. "Some of them knew the Hebrew language, too. I just read the other day about the first governor of Plymouth. His name was Governor Bradford. He knew how to read and write Hebrew."

"Tell me some more about the first Pilgrims," Hillel asked.

"Many years after the Jews came to Palestine they built a beautiful Temple. They came to visit the Temple in Jerusalem for three holidays, three times a year. Can you name them, Hillel?"

"Let me think a minute. Sukos, of course, is one. Passover was another. Was the third Purim?" Hillel thought a minute. "No, it was Shovuos."

"Right!" said Susan. "Those days were very busy and crowded days in Jerusalem. Families came from all over Palestine. Others came from far-off

73

lands like Egypt and Babylonia—wherever Jews were living."

"That must have been exciting," said Hillel.

"Oh, yes. Many of them had to sleep out-of-doors. They cooked out-of-doors, too. Just imagine. There must have been something like a trailer park outside of Jerusalem. Instead of automobiles, there were ox-carts and chariots and horses and mules and camels and donkeys. Instead of trailers, there were tents. And then, early on the morning of the festival, the men and women and children dressed in their best clothes and went up the mountain to the Temple. On the way they were met by Priests and Levites. They took the Pilgrims to the Temple, singing songs and playing on harps and other musical instruments. At the Temple, the Priests made sacrifices and thanked God for the good harvest."

"And did the Pilgrims in Plymouth know about this?"

"Of course they did."

"When did the Pilgrims come to Plymouth?" asked Hillel.

"You should know that—in 1620."

Hillel was doing some figuring on his paper. Then he said, slowly, "That means that for more than three hundred years, Americans have been celebrating a holiday which began in the land of Palestine three thousand years ago. American Jews should be proud to know that."

"We are," said Susan. "Now, I think you must stop talking. Your mother said talking is not good for your sore throat."

"My throat!" Hillel was surprised. "My throat feels much better. And I feel fine. I'm not unhappy any more."

"Do you think you could nap now?" asked Susan.

Hillel was willing to try. Susan fixed his bedcovers. She pulled down the window shades and left the room.

Hillel closed his eyes. He thought about pilgrims, about chariots and ox-carts, about Indians, about the Temple. Hillel stopped thinking. He was asleep.

A Different Chanuko

Hillel and Stanley were doing their homework together. They were sitting at Hillel's desk. It was a good idea to work together. When they had arithmetic problems, Stanley helped Hillel. When they had grammar to do, Hillel helped Stanley.

The last arithmetic problem was solved. Hillel closed his notebook with a bang. "I am glad that is finished," he said. "Now let's clean up the desk and go downstairs for milk and cookies."

Stanley picked up his papers and books. He began to put them into his school bag.

"Wait a minute," cried Hillel. "You are taking my luach." The luach always stood at the back of the desk. It must have fallen forward and Stanley had picked it up with his tablet. He had it in his hand.

"I'm sorry," said Stanley. "I didn't notice. What is it, a sort of calendar? I never saw one like that before. It is very pretty."

"It comes from the State of Israel," Hillel explained. He told Stanley all about the luach and his visit to the Jewish bookstore.

"Let's find the next holiday on the luach," said Stanley.

Hillel turned a page on the luach. "The next holiday will soon be here. It is Chanuko. You see there is a whole week of red-letter days. We talked about Chanuko in religious school last week. Don't you remember?"

"I had a cold last Sunday. I couldn't go to

school." Stanley kept staring at the calendar in his hand. He was thinking hard. Suddenly he said, "Hillel, I want to ask you something. I need some help."

Of course Hillel was ready to help Stanley. He was his best friend.

"We have never lit the Chanuko candles in our home. My Mother and Dad used to live in a very small town when they were children. They did not go to religious school. They did not know about the holidays. Now that we live here, things are different. This is the first year I am going to religious school. Mother and Dad are happy that we go together."

"I am glad, too," said Hillel. "It's fun to have a friend."

"I would like to celebrate Chanuko at home," Stanley went on. "I think Mother and Dad would like it, too. But I will need a *menorah* and Chanuko candles. What should I do?"

"You could buy a menorah at the Jewish bookstore. Mr. Levine would help you choose it. Will you have enough money for a menorah?"

"I think so. My bank is pretty full. I will give the menorah to Mother and Dad for a Chanuko present. I hope they like it. And I will light the candles myself every night."

"The Jewish bookstore is downtown. When can you go there?"

"Next week I have to go to the dentist. I can go to the bookstore then."

"Do you know the blessings?" asked Hillel.

"No," Stanley answered. "But I am sure we will study them at school. And you can help me."

Hillel was able to help Stanley right away. He had a card with the Chanuko blessings and the Chanuko songs printed on it. His religious school teacher had given one to everyone in the class. He took it out of his school bag and gave it to Stanley.

"I will ask for my card on Sunday," said Stanley. "Then I will have one for Mother and Dad, and one for myself. We can say the blessings and sing 'Rock of Ages' together. I hope I will learn the blessings."

"Of course you will," said Hillel. "We will practice them together. Joseph knows them very well. When we have studied them, he can listen to us. If we make mistakes, he will correct them."

"I am going right home," said Stanley. "I am too excited to drink milk. I want to see how much money I have in my bank. I can hardly wait to go to the bookstore to buy a menorah. This Chanuko will be a different Chanuko for me."

79

A Night to Remember

The first Chanuko candle shone brightly. Next to it the shamos twinkled. Chanuko had just begun. The blessings were said and the songs were sung. Everything was just the way it had been the year before.

No, one thing was different. Stanley was absent. He was at home. Tonight he would light his own Chanuko candles. This was the night he had been waiting for, for almost three weeks.

Hillel had promised to come over to Stanley's house as soon as possible. Stanley would wait for him.

"May I go to Stanley's now?" Hillel asked. "He wants me to watch him light his first Chanuko Menorah."

"Of course," said Mother. "You will have a good time. Be sure to take Stanley's Chanuko present with you."

How could Hillel forget? He had thought a long time before he chose Stanley's gift. Then he decided to give Stanley two gifts. Stanley liked puzzles. When Hillel went to the toy shop to pick out his presents for Joseph and Leah, he found a very interesting puzzle for Stanley. But that was not all. He had another idea. He would give Stanley a luach. Mother brought one home from the Jewish bookstore. That is how Hillel had two Chanuko gifts for Stanley.

Stanley's house was just next door. Hillel put on his coat and stepped outside. It was very dark. But light streamed out from the windows of one house and met the light which came out from the windows of the other. Hillel ran across the yard in a path of light and rang Stanley's bell.

Stanley was waiting for him. He took him into his room at the back of the house. "Dad isn't here yet," he said. "I am waiting for him to come home. When we hear him come in, we will take everything into the dining-room."

"Where is your menorah?" asked Hillel.

Stanley opened the closet. On a high shelf was a brass menorah. It looked brand new. The brass holders sparkled.

"It is beautiful," said Hillel. "Are you sure it is a surprise?"

"Of course," Stanley replied. "I kept it hidden for two weeks. Mr. Levine packed it very well for me. I opened the package this afternoon. Mother and Dad don't know about it at all."

They heard Stanley's mother coming toward them. Stanley quickly closed the closet door.

"How are you, Hillel?" asked Mrs. Stern. "Will you stay and eat dinner with us? Stanley's father will be home very soon."

"No, thank you," Hillel answered. "I just came over for a few minutes."

"All right. But be sure to see me before you go home."

Stanley and Hillel were surprised. Why did Mrs. Stern want to see Hillel again? He came over nearly every day. Sometimes he saw Stanley's mother and sometimes he did not.

"I have the Chanuko candles, too," said Stanley. He opened the lower drawer in his chest and took out a box of candles. The box said, "Forty-four candles for the Festival of Chanuko."

Hillel began to add, "One, plus two, plus three." He went up to "plus eight." "That makes only thirty-six. Why are there forty-four?"

"You forgot the shamos. One more candle each night for the shamos means eight more candles. That is why we need forty-four Chanuko candles."

Just then the front door opened. "That's Dad,"

whispered Stanley. "Let's get ready." He stood on a chair and handed the menorah to Hillel. He opened the box of yellow Chanuko candles.

Stanley placed one candle in its holder. One candle for the first night. He picked out another candle for the shamos.

"Come in, boys," called Mrs. Stern. "Dad is home."

Hillel opened the door. Stanley walked down the hall, carefully carrying the menorah in his hands. The two boys stepped into the dining-room.

They took just one step forward. Then they stopped. For a moment they stood as still as statues. They could not move. They could not speak.

On the dining-room table stood a Chanuko Menorah with the first candle waiting to be lit. In Mr. Stern's hand was the shamos.

Then everyone spoke at once. "You wanted to surprise us," cried Stanley's parents.

"You wanted to surprise me," cried Stanley. He ran in and put his menorah on the table. He turned to his parents. His mother folded him in her arms. His father thumped him on the back.

"Come in, Hillel," called Mr. Stern. "What do you think of this!"

"Stanley has made us very happy by going to religious school," said Mrs. Stern. "We want to be a happy Jewish family. We want to enjoy the holidays together. Stanley has learned a lot from you and your family."

"Stanley can light the Chanuko lights," said Hillel. "He has learned all the blessings."

"We will light them together," said Stanley's father. "I have studied them, too."

"Praised be Thou, O Lord our God, King of the universe, who hast commanded us to light the lights of Chanuko." Stanley's voice rang out true and clear. Mr. Stern's voice was a strong echo. Then they said the second Chanuko blessing. "Praised be Thou, O Lord, our God, King of the universe, who did wonderful things for our fathers at this season in those days." The last blessing was *She-he-che-yonu.* "Praised be Thou, O Lord, our God, King of the

universe, who hast permitted us to be present at this happy time." Then they all sang "Rock of Ages." It was a happy time.

Mrs. Stern turned to Hillel. "Come closer, Hillel," she said. "We want to share our Chanuko joy with you."

Hillel came over and took Stanley's hand. He knew something wonderful was happening for Stanley and his parents. He understood why Mrs. Stern had asked him to stay. He wanted to run home to tell Mother and Father. He wanted them to share in it, too. This was a night to remember.

The Surprise

We're getting home late today," said Joseph to Hillel. The boys had gone to the playfield after school. Now they were coming home.

They walked up the front steps and Joseph opened the door. "How dark it is. Where is everybody?" He called, "Mother, where are you?"

Instead of Mother, Leah answered. She ran down the steps to meet them. "Mother isn't home. She left us a note. Here it is."

Joseph read the note. It said:

Dear children:
I had to go to see Grandma. She has a cold. Daddy and I will come home together at six o'clock. Be good.
Love,
Mother

"That's too bad," said Hillel. "I hope Grandma will feel better soon." He went into his room and took off his wraps. He put his books on the desk next to his luach. Without thinking, he picked it up.

Joseph went to his room. He wanted to begin

to study. Suddenly he heard a cry, "Joseph, Leah. Come here quick."

"What's the matter, Hillel?" they cried, running into Hillel's room.

Hillel was standing with the calendar in his hand. "Look at this," he said. "Today is a holiday. It is marked in red. It's Tu Bi-Sh'vot."

"That's the New Year for Trees," said Joseph. "We talked about it in religious school. I forgot it was today. It's good the calendar reminded us."

"I wonder if Mother forgot, too," said Hillel.

Leah had another idea. "Maybe she was going to surprise us and then she couldn't because she had to go to Grandma's."

"You must be right," agreed Joseph. "Mother always has something special for Tu Bi-Sh'vot. What a shame. Now everything is spoiled."

Hillel was quiet. He was thinking hard. Suddenly he cried, "No, it isn't spoiled. Why can't we fix a Tu Bi-Sh'vot party for Mother and Daddy? We will make the surprise for them."

"What do we need for a Tu Bi-Sh'vot party?" asked Leah.

"I know," said Joseph. "In the Land of Israel it is warm now. The trees are beginning to bloom. You're supposed to eat the fruits that grow there

and say the blessings, too. We need oranges—"

"And dates and figs," said Hillel.

"And almonds," added Leah.

"How about raisins?" asked Hillel. "And what about those black sticks with pits in them. We had some last year."

"Those are carob beans. I don't know where to

get them," said Joseph, sadly. "But first let's see what's in the refrigerator."

The children ran down to the kitchen. They opened the refrigerator. There were lots of oranges in a basket. "There are oranges and a large package of dates."

"Mother has raisins on the shelf," called Leah. "She gave me some yesterday."

"Let's give everyone a holiday plate," said Hillel. "We should have almonds, too."

"I can run to the grocery store to get some," said Joseph. He began to search his pockets. "I have only ten cents."

"See what you have in your bank," said Hillel. "I will look, too."

"So will I," said Leah.

Hillel had only twenty-four cents in his bank. All his savings had gone for Chanuko presents. Joseph had twenty cents more. "We will not have enough," he said.

Then Leah ran in. Her hands were full of pennies. "Count them. There are a lot." Yes, there were sixty pennies.

"Take them all," said Leah.

"We will give you our share," promised Hillel and Joseph, "as soon as we save it up."

90

Joseph ran out. He had to hurry to be back before Mother and Daddy came home.

Hillel and Leah went into the dining-room. They put a clean tablecloth on the table. They took out the company dishes and glasses. They found two of Mother's plants with green leaves hanging over the flower pots and put them in the center of the table.

"You begin to fill the Tu Bi-Sh'vot plates," said Hillel. "I will print a sign."

Leah put a pretty glass plate at each place. She picked out the largest oranges, the fattest dates, and the juiciest raisins.

"Look what I found," cried Hillel. He came running into the room. In his hands were some small green wooden trees. "They are from our Land of the Bible game. We can put them on the table, too. And here is the sign. Let's hang it over the door."

This is the sign that Hillel printed:

The front door opened. Joseph came in. He carried a large package. "Here are almonds and figs. And what do you think? I bought some carob beans. Mr. Weiner told me about the carob beans. When he was a boy and he and his friend played games, they used the seeds for counting. And he told me something else. The carob tree is a very ancient tree. In olden times, people used the seeds as weights on a scale, and the fruit for food for themselves and for their cattle. It's too bad I had to hurry away. He would have told me much more."

Quickly the children put the rest of the fruit on the plates. Hillel tacked up his sign. Everything was ready for the party. Now they had to wait for Mother and Daddy to come home.

They went into the living-room. It began to get dark. Only one small light was burning. Oh, how hard it was to sit still! If only Mother and Daddy would hurry.

Suddenly, there were voices outside. The children sat very still. The door opened.

"Hello, children," called Mother. "I am sorry I had to go away. But why is it so dark? Let us turn on the lights."

Father came into the living-room. He switched on the big center light. Then the children ran into the dining-room. Mother and Father followed. Hillel turned on the light there, too.

"Surprise, surprise," they called. Mother and Father stood and looked and looked. They could not say a word.

"It's Tu Bi-Sh'vot and we forgot," said Father, at last.

"The calendar told us," cried Hillel. "It was printed in red. We knew it was a holiday."

"Let us celebrate," said Father. "We will eat the fruits of the Land of the Bible and say the Hebrew blessings. Then we will sing some songs. And later on, we can play some games. Thank you, Joseph, Hillel, and Leah, for the Tu Bi-Sh'vot party."

Dan's Visit

Hillel carried the mail into the house. In his hand were three letters. Two were for Father and one was for Mother. He wished that some time there would be a letter for him. The only time he received mail was on his birthday. Then there were many postcards and letters in the mailbox all addressed to him. He would have to wait a while.

He took the letters upstairs to Mother. "Here is a letter for you, Mother," he said, "and here are two more for Daddy."

"Thank you, Hillel," said Mother. She opened her letter and began to read it.

"This letter is for the whole family," said Mother, smiling. "It is from Cousin Dan. He is coming to visit us."

That was good news. Dan was Hillel's cousin. He lived in New York. Everyone liked him, especially Joseph and Hillel and Cousin David. Dan was the oldest cousin in the family. Whenever he visited, he treated the boys to a ball game, or to the zoo or to the movies. But now his visit would be even more exciting. For Dan was in the U. S. Army. He was a corporal. Hillel ran downstairs to tell Joseph the news.

Three days later Dan arrived, just in time for the Sabbath. He was on his way to a new post. Dan was a tall, red-haired boy, with a big smile. You could not help liking him.

Dan stood with Father and the children as Mother lit the Sabbath candles and blessed them. When Mother gave each one a Sabbath kiss, she kissed him, too.

"It is good to be here for Shabos," said Dan. "We have Sabbath services in the army, but it is not like being at home."

"Let us say our Sabbath blessings first," said Father. He turned to Dan. "Would you like to recite Kiddush for us?"

"Yes, I would," answered Dan. He picked up the kiddush cup and chanted, "Let us praise God and thank Him for the blessings of this past week." He went on to finish the Kiddush. "The seventh day is the Sabbath. It is holy unto the Lord."

Dan's voice was louder than Father's. It filled the room. Everyone was very quiet until he finished. Then they sang out together, "Amen."

Father turned to Leah. It was her turn now.

95

She liked to recite the blessing over the chalo. She could say it in Hebrew and in English. When she had finished, Father gave each one a small piece of the chalo and they said, "Amen."

While the family was eating the good Sabbath dinner, Father said, "Dan, you chanted the Kiddush very well. I didn't know you have such a fine voice."

Dan laughed. His face grew a little red. "I have had some practice since I am in the army. I chant Kiddush at our Friday evening services."

"Don't you have a chaplain?" asked Father.

"Yes, we do. I am his assistant. Chanting the Kiddush is one of the ways I help him."

"What is a chaplain?" asked Hillel.

Dan explained. "A chaplain is a minister who is in the army or navy. He is in charge of the religious life of the soldiers."

"Is there a rabbi for the Jewish soldiers?" asked Joseph.

"In a large camp or on a large ship there will be separate chaplains for Jews and Christians. In a small camp there may be just a rabbi or just a minister or priest. When the chaplain is a rabbi, he will help Catholics and Protestants with their services. If a minister or a priest is the only chaplain at a post, he will help the Jews as well as the Protestants and Catholics."

"There was a time when there were only Christian chaplains. There were Jewish soldiers, but no Jewish chaplains," said Father.

"I don't understand," said Hillel. "If Jews were soldiers there should have been a chaplain for them, too."

"You are right," said Father, "and a great American President thought just as you do. He asked Congress to pass a law so that he could appoint chaplains of different religions for all the soldiers who were serving in the United States army."

"What about the Air Force?" asked Joseph.

"Who was the President?" asked Hillel.

"How did it happen?" asked Leah.

Father smiled. "What a lot of questions! I think you can answer them yourself. First I will tell you when all this happened. It was way back in the year 1861."

"There were no airplanes then," exclaimed Joseph. "I have answered my own question."

Hillel couldn't answer so quickly. He had to think about his history. "In 1861 the President was Abraham Lincoln," he said, at last.

"But I can't answer my question," said Leah. "I need some help."

"Well," said Father, "when we have finished dinner and sung our Sabbath songs, I will tell you how it happened. It is a very nice story."

The President and the Rabbi

Just as everyone was settled comfortably in the living-room, the bell rang. Cousin David came in.

"I couldn't wait," he cried. "I had to see Dan. Mother and Dad will come soon."

"You are just in time to hear a story," said Hillel. "It is about rabbis in the army. They are called chaplains."

David sat down on the floor next to Dan. He leaned his head against Dan's knees.

Father began his story:

Chaplains are not new in the army. Back in the days of the Revolutionary War, General Washington appointed chaplains for the soldiers. They were Christian ministers. There were some Jews in the army, but they were scattered. No one thought of appointing chaplains for them. In fact, there were only a few rabbis in all the colonies. They surely helped Jewish soldiers whenever they could.

You know our country began with thirteen states. But before long it grew larger. Men and women came here from all over the world. Children

99

were born. Cities grew larger. Forests were cleared. Railroads stretched from the east to the west. It was an exciting time for the young nation. Among the newcomers were many Jews. They became citizens of the United States. They loved their new country and worked for it.

Then what happened? The Civil War broke out. Thousands of soldiers went to war. Jews became soldiers, too. They fought in the armies of the North and in the armies of the South.

Congress had to pass many laws. The army had to be organized. Generals had to be named. One law was passed appointing chaplains. But the law had a fault. It said an army chaplain had to be a Christian minister. We do not think the law was written this way on purpose. We think it was a mistake.

What about the thousands of Jews who were serving in the Union Army? Shouldn't there be chaplains for them, too? Something had to be done.

One cold morning in December, 1861, President Lincoln sat in his office. In an outer room, dozens of men were crowded, each hoping for a few minutes with the President. The President's secretary came out from the inner office and crossed the room. Everyone watched as he stood before a young bearded man. "The President will see you, Rabbi Fischel."

101

The rabbi stood up, hardly believing the good news. He had come to ask the President if he could not appoint some Jewish chaplains.

The rabbi entered the inner office. He stood for a moment at the President's desk. Mr. Lincoln looked up. He was kind and courteous. Rabbi Fischel was not afraid. He felt he was speaking to a friend. He told the President of his errand.

President Lincoln had much work to do and many problems to solve. But he listened quietly to the rabbi. He asked some questions. He promised to think about the matter.

"Come back to see me tomorrow, Rabbi Fischel," he said. "I will try to have an answer for you."

The next day the President was busier than ever. He had some special visitors from foreign lands. Rabbi Fischel waited a long time. He was ready to leave. He was disappointed. Just then someone touched him on his arm. It was the President's secretary. "I have a message for you. Today the President will tell the Cabinet what you have asked for."

Arnold Fischel walked away from the White House. He thought of Jews in America and of Jews in other parts of the world. In those days there was hardly another place in the whole world where a Jew could speak simply and directly to the head of his government. There was hardly another country where he could ask for something and hope to receive it. The rabbi's heart swelled with gratitude.

Later, a note was brought to his hotel. It was signed, "A. Lincoln." A. Lincoln, President of the United States, was writing to Arnold Fischel, citizen of the United States.

President Lincoln said, "I shall try to have a new law passed by Congress."

Rabbi Fischel was satisfied. He believed in the President. But he did not wait idly. He visited camps and hospitals. He helped soldiers who were ill or needed advice. He had not been appointed. He acted on his own as a Jewish chaplain.

Sometimes it takes a long time, many months, even years, for Congress to pass a law. There are many steps to take. This time Congress worked quickly. In only five months a law was passed. The new law made it possible to appoint Jewish chaplains in hospitals.

President Lincoln acted in accordance with the new law. He appointed three chaplains without delay.

They were the first Jewish chaplains appointed

according to law by a President of the United States. Many others followed. There were chaplains to serve Jewish soldiers in World War I and in World War II and in the Korean War. They served at home and overseas. They served in camps, and on board ships, and in airfields. They helped Jewish men to observe the Sabbath and the holidays. When a soldier was in trouble, he could come to the chaplain. Some chaplains gave their lives in the service of their country. They have made a fine record for themselves. There are chaplains in our armed forces today.

"Dan helps his chaplain," cried Joseph. "We are proud of him."

"I just thought of something," said Hillel. "You told us a story about President Lincoln and we will celebrate his birthday next week. It was a very good time to hear about him."

The Spice-Box

It all happened because Leah stood on a wobbly chair. She should have taken the small step stool. It had only two steps. She could climb it easily.

It was Friday afternoon. Everything seemed to be going wrong. Leah's friend, Ruthie, had a cold. She couldn't come over to play after school. Leah was tired of all her games and her books.

"Give me something to do," she begged Mother.

Mother had to think. She was all ready for Shabos. She was waiting to take a cake out of the oven. The table was set. The candlesticks were shining brightly. What could Leah do?

Mother thought about the Sabbath. Tomorrow, just before it was over, Father would say Havdolo. It was the prayer which separates the Sabbath from the rest of the week. Father used many things for Havdolo. He put wine in a kiddush cup. He lit a long, braided candle. He picked up a spice-box and smelled the fragrant spices. They reminded him of the sweetness of the Sabbath. He said a blessing for the wine, for the spices, and for lighting the candle.

105

He said farewell to the Sabbath until next week.

"Bring in the spice-box, Leah," said Mother. "Let's see if there are enough spices in it to smell sweetly when we say Havdolo tomorrow night."

The spice-box was kept in a drawer in the buffet. Leah ran into the dining-room and opened the drawer. She saw many things there—the kiddush cup, the prayer book, the chalo cover and the long candle. But not the spice-box. Where could it be?

Leah looked all around. She knew what the spice-box looked like. It was made of olive wood and had the word "Jerusalem" printed on it. On top there was a little wooden flag. .

There it was, on a shelf in the cabinet. The cabinet had a glass door. It was locked with a key. Leah could just reach the key. She opened the door. The spice-box was too high for her.

Leah ran to get her little play chair. It was not very strong. The legs were wobbly. When she stood on it she teetered back and forth. She reached for the spice-box. She had it in her hand. She closed the glass door and locked it. She twirled the box in her hand. The little wooden flag went round and round.

All of a sudden there was a loud crack. One of the legs of the play chair snapped in two. Down went Leah together with the spice-box.

"Mother, Mother," she cried.

Mother came running in. "What's the matter? Are you hurt?" She picked Leah up. No, she was not hurt. She felt all right. But where was the spice-box? They began to look. It lay under the cabinet. Mother picked it up. Her face was sad. The spice-box was broken. The little wooden flag was cracked and the little door was off its hinges.

"What shall we do?" asked Leah. "It's all my fault. We need the spice-box for tomorrow night. We cannot say Havdolo without the spice-box."

"Don't be upset," said Mother. "We will ask Grandma to lend us her beautiful silver spice-box. Hillel or Joseph can go over and get it when they get home from school. You may call up Grandma and ask her for it."

Leah knew Grandma's number. She knew how to dial the telephone. In a moment she was speaking to Grandma.

"Hello, Leah," said Grandma: "How are you? Can I do something for you?"

"I broke our wooden spice-box," said Leah. "May we borrow the silver spice-box?"

"Of course," said Grandma. "It is on the book-shelf. Just a minute."

Leah remembered the shelf with many beauti-

107

ful objects on it. Standing upright was a Seder plate with pictures of Moses and the Children of Israel. Around the edge was the Hebrew blessing for matso. Next to it stood the Chanuko Menorah, and a silver box for the esrog. Grandma also had a pair of old candlesticks. Of course, the spice-box would be there, too.

Grandma was speaking again. "I don't see the spice-box. Where can it be? I always keep it next to the candlesticks. It came from Jerusalem many years ago. It cannot be lost."

"Did you lend it to anyone else?" asked Leah.

"Lend it?" Grandma wondered. Leah held the telephone and waited.

"Yes, of course. You are right, Leah. Joseph took it to religious school. The boys in his class wanted to see it. You will have to get it at the temple annex. Ask Mother if you may go."

Leah hung up the telephone. She told Mother about the spice-box. "Shall I go to the temple annex for it?" she asked.

"Yes," said Mother. "You may go. It is only a block away. Go in to Miss Heller's office. I will give you a note for her."

Mother wrote a note. Leah put on her coat. She ran down the steps and started up the street to the temple annex. That was where the religious school had its classes. The temple was much further away.

She went to the school entrance. Miss Heller's office was there. The door was closed, but Leah reached for the knob. It did not turn. The door was locked. Leah looked in the window. The room was dark. Miss Heller must have gone home for Shabos.

Leah was unhappy. She thought about Havdolo. Everyone enjoyed it. After Father said the blessings, everyone had a sip of wine. The lights went on. Then they all sang a special song. Perhaps Father could say Havdolo anyway, but it would not be quite as nice without the spice-box.

Leah could not help herself. She began to cry as she walked slowly back to the house.

"Leah, Leah," a voice called. "Wait for me." Hillel was calling. "Why are you crying?" he asked. "Please tell me."

Leah told him about the broken spice-box. "And now it is getting late. It will soon be Shabos."

"Don't cry," said Hillel. "I have an idea. Perhaps we can make our own spice-box."

"Don't make fun of me," said Leah. "How can we make a spice-box?"

"It won't be a silver spice-box and it won't be a wooden spice-box, but it will be a spice-box all the same."

By this time they had reached their house. The children opened the door quietly and went upstairs. Mother did not hear them. They went to Leah's room.

"Where is your kindergarten envelope?" asked Hillel. "The one you brought home from religious school?"

All the children in Leah's class had received a large envelope. In it were many things—pictures and stories, cardboard cutouts, and crayons and colored papers. Leah found hers right away. She gave it to Hillel. He began to look through it quickly.

"I knew it. Here it is," he shouted. He took out a thin sheet of yellow cardboard. "It is a cutout of a Havdolo box. We can make it right away."

Leah got out her scissors and her crayons. Hillel carefully cut out the Havdolo box. Then he cut out the flag on the top of the box. While Hillel fitted the pieces and pasted them together, Leah colored the flag orange. Then Hillel took a pin and stuck the flag on the top of the spice-box. It was finished. It stood on its paper legs.

"It is not very strong, but it will last through the Sabbath. Come, let us show it to Mother."

The children ran down the stairs. They made a lot of noise. Mother came out of the kitchen. "When did you come in? I didn't hear you."

Leah couldn't wait to answer Mother. "The temple annex was closed. But we made our own spice-box. Do you like it?"

Mother looked at the cardboard spice-box. "It is very nice," she said. "We will take good care of it. Father will use it when he says Havdolo tomorrow night. He will say farewell to the Sabbath. He will welcome the week that is coming. We will sing our special song—'A good week, a week of peace.'"

Mother took the spice-box in her hand and walked into the dining-room. The children followed. She opened the glass door of the cabinet. She placed the spice-box on the middle shelf. It was right in front. There it stood, the yellow spice-box with its orange flag for all to see.

Hillel's Birthday

Hillel's birthday was only three days off. He would be nine years old. He could hardly wait. He knew there would be many surprises and gifts for him.

Hillel was sitting near his little desk. He picked up his English calendar and put a big red X on his birthday. Then he had another idea. He decided to find his Hebrew birthday on the luach.

His birthday was the 17th of March. According to the luach it was the 7th of Ador. Hillel knew about Ador. Purim was celebrated in Ador.

"I wonder if anything interesting happened on the 7th of Ador?" he thought. "I'll have to ask Daddy tonight."

He examined the page. Yes, there was Purim. It was on the 14th of Ador, just one week after his birthday.

What a shame he wasn't born on Purim. Perhaps he would have been named Mordecai. Hillel considered that for a moment. No, he was satisfied with his name. He knew Hillel was the name of a great rabbi and teacher. Rabbi Hillel lived thousands of years ago. Father had told him many stories about wise Rabbi Hillel. No, Hillel decided, he did not want to change his name.

"I was looking in my luach," said Hillel to Father when he came home. "I found out my Hebrew birthday. It's the 7th of Ador."

"You mean it's the 7th of Ador this year," Joseph corrected him.

"That's funny," said Leah. "His birthday is the same every year, isn't it?"

"This is a little hard to explain," said Father. "First bring down your luach."

Hillel ran upstairs and fetched his luach. He gave it to Father. Father saw that Hillel was right. The 17th of March was the 7th of Ador.

"And Purim is exactly one week later," said Hillel, "on the 14th of Ador. That is the 24th of March."

"Let me show you something," said Father. The children crowded around him. He turned the pages of the luach, page by page. There were two months by the name of Ador.

"Does anyone remember when Purim was last year?" he asked.

At first the children were silent. Then Joseph said, "I remember. I was Haman in the play in religious school. It was in February. But this year it is in March."

"How is that?" asked Hillel.

"Think a minute about your Hebrew calendar. Do you remember what I told you about the moon year and the sun year? The moon year has only 354 days. The sun year has 365 days."

"I remember," cried Joseph. "The moon year has eleven days less than the sun year, and we have to have . . ."

"A leap month! I remember, too," came from Hillel.

"This year we are having a leap month. It is Ador. There is the first Ador and the second Ador. Purim always comes on the 14th of Ador. In leap years it is celebrated on the 14th day of the second Ador. That is why it is sometimes in February and sometimes in March."

"Does my birthday skip around, too?" asked Hillel.

"What do you think? If the 14th of Ador changes each year on the English calendar, don't you think the 7th of Ador will change, too?"

"I guess it does. Now what shall I do? When is my birthday?"

"It is not such a problem. You must decide.

115

Which birthday will you choose? You can have your Hebrew birthday or your English birthday."

Hillel began to think. There were many things to consider. In public school, he had to give his English birthday. In religious school they asked for his English birthday. And what about his birthday party and presents? No one would know when to give him birthday gifts if he chose the Hebrew date.

"I think I'd better keep my English date," he said, slowly. "But I won't forget that I have a Hebrew birthday, too."

"That is a sensible answer," said Father. "Our every-day life follows the English calendar. Years ago, in Europe and in Palestine, Jews followed the Hebrew calendar. Many of them knew only their Hebrew birthday. I am sure that Grandpa can tell you his Hebrew birthday. He will not have to look in the luach."

Later on, Joseph and Leah found their Hebrew birthdays. They marked them on their calendars. Everyone was feeling very cheerful.

Then Hillel remembered. "I have a question to ask you," he said. "I thought of it when I marked the 7th of Ador for my birthday. I want to know if anything special happened on that day."

"I do know something interesting about the

116

7th of Ador," said Father. "But I am not sure it is true. It is a legend, a sort of story."

"We always want to hear a story," said Leah. "Please tell us."

"This is the legend about the 7th of Ador. It is that Moses was born on the 7th of Ador. Of course, we cannot be sure."

"Even so, it is an important day," said Joseph.

"But that isn't all," Father went on. "You know that Moses led the Children of Israel out of Egypt. He was their leader for forty years. One day he left them and climbed up Mount Pisgah. From the mountain-top he looked across the land of Canaan. That was the Promised Land. God had promised it to Abraham for the Children of Israel. Moses never came down from the mountain. He died on the top of the mountain. Can you guess what day that was?"

"The 7th of Ador?" guessed Hillel.

"Yes, the legend says that Moses was born and Moses died on the 7th of Ador."

"Let us mark it on every luach," said Hillel. "It is a day with an important story."

Special Purims

We have a new Sunday school teacher," said Hillel one afternoon. He was sitting in the kitchen munching on a carrot. "She came this afternoon."

"Why do you say Sunday school?" asked Leah. "Today is Tuesday."

Hillel laughed. "I don't know. It really isn't Sunday school. I go on Sunday and Tuesday, and Joseph goes on Sunday, Tuesday, and Thursday."

"Call it religious school," said Mother. "It used to be a Sunday school. But the rabbi and the teachers and the parents had a meeting. We all agreed that it was important for the children to go more often. There is so much to learn. How can you learn about the Jewish religion, Jewish history and the Jewish people, and study Hebrew, too, if you go to school only once a week?" Mother stopped short. She laughed. "I forgot, Hillel. It is really your turn to speak. Tell us about your new teacher."

"She has a Hebrew name. It is Aviva. It means spring. She told us to call her Miss Aviva."

"Call her Miss Springtime," Leah sang out.

"We were talking about Purim. Miss Aviva told us something very interesting. I never knew it before."

Mother was shelling peas, she carried the bowl over to the table. Leah sat down next to her. She opened a large pea pod. Five fat, bright green peas were in the pod. She dropped them into the bowl, one by one.

"What did Miss Aviva tell you?" asked Mother.

"Purim is coming in two weeks," Hillel began.

"That isn't new," said Leah. "We all know that."

"Go on, Hillel," said Mother. "Let us listen, Leah."

"The Purim we celebrate then isn't the only Purim. That is, it isn't the only time that Jews remember a day when they were saved from harm. There were other times when they were in trouble, and suddenly they were saved, just like on Purim."

"How many times?" asked Leah.

"Nobody knows exactly," Hillel answered. "One writer made up a list of forty different days. Each one is a special Purim. They have special names. Wait a minute. I wrote them down in my notebook. I will get it."

Hillel ran upstairs to get his notebook. He came back turning the pages over.

119

"Here it is. There are all kinds of names. Some Purims are named after a city. Some are named for people. And listen to this. One Purim is named, 'The Purim of the Bandits.' One is called, 'The Purim of the Wonderful Bomb.'"

"That must be exciting," cried Leah. "Tell me about it." She stopped shelling peas. They would have to wait.

"I don't know it. Miss Aviva didn't have time to tell it. She said she would tell us some of the Purim stories next week."

"I can't wait," said Leah. "I shall ask Daddy tonight. Do you think he knows?"

"If you ask him," said Mother, "he will look for the story in one of his books. Then he can tell you about it after he has read it."

"Let's do our homework now," said Hillel. "Then we'll have time to hear the story tonight."

A Purim Miracle

Father came home early from work. He was tired. He had been busy all day. He had to go to a meeting at night.

Mother said to him, "Lie down. You can rest for a while before we eat dinner. I will ask the children to be quiet."

Joseph and Hillel and Leah were very quiet. Each one went into his room. Each was busy with his school work.

Later on, Mother said to Leah, "Call Daddy. Tell him dinner is ready."

Leah knocked on the bedroom door. She said softly, "Daddy, it is time for dinner."

Father called cheerily, "Come in, Leah." Leah walked into the bedroom. Father was smiling. "I had a good nap. You were all very quiet. I am not tired any more."

When dinner was over, Leah said, "Daddy isn't tired any more. Maybe he will tell us the story—the story about the bomb."

Father was surprised. "A story about a bomb?"

Hillel explained about the special Purims. Father thought for a few minutes. Then he said, "I remember the story. It is in one of my books. Wait a few minutes. I shall have to read it over again. I shall just have time to tell it to you before I go to the meeting."

Father picked out a heavy book from the bookcase. He turned the pages quickly. He began to read.

Then he called, "Come here, children. I have found the story. We will give it your name. 'The Purim of the Wonderful Bomb.' It is a true story. One thing is very strange about it. It is called a special Purim, but it happened on Passover."

This is the story Father told:

"This happened almost two hundred years ago in a city in Italy. At that time, the Jews had to live in a special part of every city. It was called the Ghetto. A high wall separated the ghetto from the rest of the city. During the day, the Jews could leave the ghetto. Some men went to work. Others had little shops outside the ghetto. Sometimes a woman had an errand in the city. In the evening all the Jews came home. They walked through the ghetto gates. A guard locked the gates behind them. They could not go out again until morning.

"The French and Italians were at war. Outside

the city, the French troops were waiting for a chance to capture it. The French soldiers were friendly to the Jews. When they came into a city, they tore down the walls of the ghetto. The Jews could move freely about the city. They could live in any part of the city that they chose.

"Night after night, the cannon roared. The French were firing on the Italian city.

"Days passed. The holiday of Passover arrived. In the tiny ghetto synagogue building, on an upper floor, the Jews gathered for services. But outside the gates of the ghetto something terrible was happening. Among the Italians a group of wicked men were getting ready to attack the Jews while they were praying. In their hands were sticks and stones and guns.

"The gates of the ghetto were forced open. The wicked men rushed in. They ran down the long narrow streets of the ghetto. They threw stones into windows. Some men carried lighted torches. They were ready to start a fire.

"Soon they were outside the synagogue. Upstairs the Jews were saying their Passover prayers, remembering how God had appointed Moses to lead the Hebrews out of Egypt. Down below stood the angry men. What would happen? Suddenly, there

124

was a terrible noise. From outside the city, the French army had sent a cannon ball crashing through the night air. It hit the wall of the synagogue.

"In the ghetto street, the crowd became very frightened. The next shot from the cannon might hit them. They threw down their sticks and stones. They ran away as fast as they could. They used the torches to light the way. They did not start a fire. They shouted, 'A bomb has exploded!'

"Then all was quiet. Only one bomb fell—the one that hit the synagogue. It did not hurt anyone. It only made a great hole in the wall. The Jews were very lucky.

"The rabbi and the cantor went on with the service. They said prayers of thanks to God for saving the Jews from the cannon and from the anger of the mob.

"The hole in the wall was never repaired. The rabbi of the town wrote a poem about the wonderful event. He wrote of their own special Purim, when they were saved from harm by the bomb. Every year, during Passover, the poem was recited. As the Jews listened to the poem, they could look through the hole in the wall which the bomb had made. It is there to this very day."

125

"To this very day," Hillel repeated.

"Yes," said Father, "and around the hole is a circle of Hebrew words written in golden letters. They say, 'The Miracle of the Bomb.'"

THE MIRACLE of the BOMB

Hidden Treasures

Something special was happening in Hillel's class at religious school. They had a visitor. He was an archeologist. His name was Dr. Simon.

Miss Aviva introduced Dr. Simon. She explained that an archeologist is a man who visits ancient lands to study the history of bygone days. He tries to discover the places where old buried cities may be found. In these old cities there are remains of homes and palaces and city walls.

Then Dr. Simon began to speak. This is what he told the class:

"An archeologist is something like a detective. He is seeking hidden treasure. He usually works with a team of men who are experts. One of them may be an architect. One is a photographer. One is usually a historian. They also need a band of workers to help with the digging.

"All over the ancient land there are small hills. They are not natural hills of earth and rock. These are hills or mounds made by buried cities or villages. Such a hill is called a *tel*.

"Let's suppose that long, long ago a village was built at a certain place. In this dry country, it would probably be near a stream of water. People lived in the village. They built houses. They built a wall to protect themselves. Then something happened. Perhaps there was a drought or a famine. The people left in search of food and water. Or enemies came. There was a battle. Families fled from their homes. The village became empty. It was destroyed. Winds came and covered the city with dust. The rains softened the mud huts, and they fell apart. The village wall broke down, brick by brick.

"Years passed by. A new tribe came into the area. They wanted to settle down with their families. This was a good place. The stream was inviting. They cleared away some of the dirt of the first village. If it was all covered over, they built their houses and their city wall right over it. For years the tribe lived happily. Then once again the place was destroyed or deserted. And once again when time had gone by, a new village was built over the same site.

"Now we come to our own times. The archeologist and his team are searching in the area. They see a huge mound—a tel. In the earth or sand nearby, they find pieces of old pottery. They recognize the shape and the color of the pottery. They have seen

other pottery like it. It tells them a story. It comes from long ago. Perhaps this is the place to dig. The photographer takes pictures from different sides of the tel. The architect studies the pictures. They have a meeting to talk things over. They decide to dig.

"You would think that they would begin digging at the top to uncover the whole first layer. No. That is not the way the archeologist works. To him the tel is like a layer cake, like the one your mother bakes for Shabos. Of course, it is a little larger. He wants to cut a wedge out of the layer cake, so that he can look inside and see each village, one on top of the other. The newest village is at the top. The oldest village is at the very bottom.

"One famous archeologist found a tel which had a layer of sixteen villages or small cities, one on top of the other. The earliest city was over three thousand years old. Layer after layer told a different story. The archeologist and his team learned what kind of people lived in the villages; whether they were warriors or peace-loving folk; whether they had a king; what kind of a god they worshipped, and many, many more important facts."

Dr. Simon stopped speaking. Miss Aviva looked around. She had never seen the pupils so still. Each one seemed to be holding his breath.

"Now you may ask questions," she said.

Nearly every hand shot up. There were many questions to ask Dr. Simon. They followed thick and fast.

"How can you tell how old a city is?"

"What kind of things are found?"

"What is the reason for studying old cities?"

"What was happening three thousand years ago?"

Dr. Simon was very pleased. He was glad the class was so interested in what he had told them. He began to answer the questions.

"Hundreds of pieces of pottery are usually found in an old city. It is often possible to join the pieces and form a whole jug or a bowl from them. These bits of pottery are our calendar. They may be like pottery which was found in other places where archeologists have dug before, and where the date of a city has already been discovered. Different kinds of pottery belong to different times. How would they get from one place to another? Let's suppose a city was a seaport. Sailors carried dishes and water jugs to places far away. They were sold there, and others like them were made by their new owners.

"Sometimes small clay tablets are found, with writing on them. A clay seal may have the mark of

131

a ruler on it. Scholars recognize the writing or the names of kings and cities. These also tell us when people lived in a city.

"Many different kinds of articles are found. Clay tablets, water jugs, jewelry, knives and forks, statues, pieces of spears and javelins, oil lamps and altars for sacrifices. From them we learn almost everything about the people who lived in these ancient cities.

"Now the most important question of all—what good does archeology do? To answer that, I must repeat one of your own questions. What story in Jewish history took place about three thousand years ago? We shall soon celebrate a holiday connected with it."

For a moment no one answered. Then Hillel remembered. He had looked at his luach in the morning and he knew. He raised his hand.

"Passover is the holiday. It is only three weeks off And I think the story must be about the Hebrews leaving Egypt with their leader, Moses."

"You are right," said Dr. Simon. "The Bible tells the story of Moses and how he led the Hebrews out of Egypt. We believe that happened about thirty-two hundred years ago. The Bible tells other stories of our ancestors. Some of the clay tablets and other finds which have been discovered by archeologists explain these tales. It is very exciting to learn that many stories in the Bible about our ancestors probably happened just as they are written down. People, very much like Abraham, Isaac, and Jacob, lived in these old cities, with their families and their possessions. So archeology helps us to understand the Bible and the history of our people.

"Now about Moses and the Children of Israel. The Hebrews wandered in the desert for forty years. They passed near cities and villages. It is possible that they passed by some of the villages which archeologists are digging up today. When they celebrated the first Passover in the wilderness they used vessels of long ago. Some day we may find them."

Stanley couldn't keep quiet. "Perhaps you will dig something up about Moses," he cried out.

"Archeologists in Egypt have learned much about the Pharaoh who lived at the time of Moses, the Pharaoh before whom Moses stood," answered Dr. Simon. "Yes, some day we may learn much more about Moses."

Miss Aviva thanked Dr. Simon. The class crowded around him. He had brought them bits of pottery to examine. Hillel was standing right next to him. Dr. Simon gave him a piece of pottery to hold. "This is the handle of an old water jug. It is probably the kind that the Hebrews held when Moses struck the rock for them and gave them water to drink."

Hillel looked at the piece of pottery in his hand. What a story it could tell! Perhaps a little Hebrew boy of long ago held the jug in his hands and filled it with water. What was his name? Was it Marneen like the shepherd boy in the story Daddy told them? The boy seemed real to him.

Hillel had news to tell at home. The story of Passover wasn't made up. The Bible and the Haggadah told about real men and women, and real boys and girls. He knew he would enjoy Passover more than ever this year.

134

A Passover Poem

Hillel looked at his calendar just before he ran out
of his room. Two more days to Passover. A whole
week was marked in red. What fun that would be!

Mother asked, "Are you sure you know your
poem?"

"Yes, I recited it again last night for Joseph. I
know all the verses about the sons. But I have only
one to say."

"Then be off to school and enjoy yourself."
Mother kissed all the children and they ran out.

Mother was talking about a poem that Hillel's
teacher wrote about Passover. The children of his
class were going to recite it during the school Seder.

Hillel was the second son of the Haggadah.
Everyone laughed to think he was the wicked son.
He promised to be good at the Seder.

In class, Miss Aviva decided to have a rehearsal
before the children went to the assembly for the
Seder. All the children who were reciting sat in the
front row. Four boys stood up and faced the class.
Each had one verse to say. They began:

A Holiday of Fours

There are four sons for you to meet
This week on Seder night,
I am the first whom you will greet,
I am the one called wise.

I am the second you will see,
I am the wicked son.
The holiday is not for me,
Unless I mend my ways.

The third one, I, the simple son,
Who asks, what means this night?
Explain to me what has been done
To make my people free.

The littlest one who does not know
A question must be asked,
I am the fourth, but when I grow,
I'll try to do my share.

The boys sat down, and five girls stood up before the class. The first girl began:

Ma Nishtano—the questions four,
Are asked each Seder night,
How does this evening differ,
How does it show God's might?

This was really the introduction. Then came the four questions.

On other nights we eat our bread,
And sometimes matso, too,
But why tonight, just matso crisp
Is eaten by each Jew?

And why tonight eat bitter herbs?
The sign of slavery,
The sign of cruel and bitter days,
Unhappy history.

The Seder's strange in other ways,
For twice we dip tonight.
Why? is the question I shall ask.
I hope I get it right.

Why do we lean, not sit up straight?
Is question number four.
And then the story will begin
With answers four and more.

The little girls sat down. But the poem was not finished. Two boys and two girls rose from their seats. It was their turn now:

> Again we find the number four,
> Four ways in which the Lord
> Helped Moses take the Hebrews out,
> According to His word.
>
> The Lord said, "I will bring you out,
> I shall deliver thee,
> From trouble and from slavery,
> Into a land that's free."
>
> He promised, "I will take you out,
> And you will be redeemed."
> He kept His word, though more than once,
> Impossible it seemed.
>
> And last of all, four cups of wine,
> Each one with prayer we bless,
> We raise our voices high to sing,
> In grateful happiness.

That was the end of the poem. The class clapped their hands. Everyone had recited well. No one forgot his lines.

Miss Aviva said, "That was a fine rehearsal. Now we can go down to the assembly and join the rest of the school at the Seder."

Six Months to Study

Joseph had been studying many months. He was preparing for his Bar Mitzvah.

In the beginning, Joseph thought he could be all ready for his Bar Mitzvah in a few weeks. One day the rabbi called him into his study. He said, "Sit down, Joseph. Let us talk about your Bar Mitzvah. It is time to begin to study."

Joseph was surprised. "I don't understand, rabbi," he said. "I have been coming to religious school since kindergarten. I have been studying all the time."

"You are right," said the rabbi. "You have been a good student. You have been learning Jewish history and the Bible and Hebrew. But there are special things to know when you become Bar Mitzvah. You will study them with me and I will explain them to you."

"Will it take so long?" asked Joseph. "It is November now. I will be thirteen years old in April. That is when I will be Bar Mitzvah."

The rabbi smiled. "Let us make an agreement.

We will begin to study together now the special things you must learn for your Bar Mitzvah. Whenever you feel you are ready for your Bar Mitzvah, you may stop."

Joseph thought that was a good idea. He would study for his Bar Mitzvah. It could not take very long. When he was ready, he would tell the rabbi.

"First let me tell you what being Bar Mitzvah means. The words, 'Bar Mitzvah,' are two Hebrew words which mean 'Son of the Commandment' or 'Son of the Law.' The Law is the Law of the Jewish people, the Torah. When you become Bar Mitzvah, you accept the Torah and promise to try to live up to its laws.

"Now," the rabbi went on, "we must pick out the Sabbath for your Bar Mitzvah. Then we will know which portion of the Torah will be read that morning. We will see which selection from the Prophets you will read for the Haftoro."

The rabbi took out his luach. "In our temple we like to set all Bar Mitzvah dates by the Hebrew calendar. First we must find out your Hebrew birthday," he said.

"I know my Hebrew birthday," said Joseph.

"You do!" exclaimed the rabbi. "You are the

first Bar Mitzvah boy in a long time who knew his
Hebrew birthday."

Joseph explained. He told about his luach and
Hillel's luach. He told the rabbi how all the children
had looked up their Hebrew birthdays.

The rabbi turned the pages of his luach. "You
could become Bar Mitzvah on May 9," he said. "On
that Sabbath there is a very fine reading from the
Torah. There is a splendid reading from the Prophet

141

Amos. I will write them down for you and you can tell your parents. Please ask them if May 9 will suit them. Bring me their answer tomorrow."

Mother and Father were very happy to hear the rabbi's message. "The date is fine," they said. "We are glad you are getting ready for your Bar Mitzvah."

The next day, Joseph took Hillel with him when he went to see the rabbi.

"Now that the date is settled," said the rabbi, "I will tell you about the readings from the Bible." He gave Joseph and Hillel each a Bible and found the place for them. "The Torah reading for your Sabbath, Joseph, is from the Book of Leviticus. Leviticus is the third book of the Bible. It is a book of laws. Some are hard to understand, some are easy. On the morning of your Bar Mitzvah, a very important passage will be read. I think you will recognize one of the sentences. It is, 'Thou shalt love thy neighbor as thyself.'"

Joseph cried, "We were talking about that in public school the other day. I didn't know it comes from the Bible."

"Many well-known sayings are taken from the Bible. Perhaps we shall have time to talk about them while we are studying together. Now let us find the

Haftoro reading. You will learn to read it in Hebrew. It is from the Prophet Amos. Do you know you are a very lucky boy, Joseph?"

Of course, Joseph didn't know why.

"You will have a fine reading for your Haftoro. I will tell you about it."

Joseph and Hillel settled back in their chairs to listen.

"The Prophet Amos lived about twenty-seven hundred years ago. He spoke to the people who lived in the kingdom of Israel. He believed that God had commanded him to speak to them. His message was very important. Part of it is found in the portion that you will read."

Joseph kept silent, but he was listening very carefully.

"What was the message of Amos?" asked Hillel.

"Amos said that God cares for all people, wherever they are found. He watches over the men and women and children of all the different lands and different countries, not just for one special people or one special nation. Amos was one of the very first men in the whole world to say this."

"Doesn't everyone believe that?" asked Hillel.

"Most people do now. They believe in one God, who is the Father of all mankind. But back in the days of Amos, most people believed that every nation had its own god, who cared just for that nation. Amos brought a new idea. He said that God had helped the Ethiopians and the Egyptians and the people of Aram and many other people."

Hillel asked, "Who are the Ethiopians?"

"They are an ancient people. We read about them in other parts of the Bible. Their descendants are some of the black people who live in Ethiopia on the continent of Africa."

Joseph said slowly, "Then Amos meant that God cares for other people like the Ethiopians, just as He cares for the Jewish people."

"Yes," said the rabbi. "Of course, that is only part of the message of Amos. As we read together, you will find out the rest of it."

"Now I know why it takes so long to study for my Bar Mitzvah," said Joseph. He was right. Something very strange was happening. Six months wasn't a long time at all. He needed all of it.

The first special Bar Mitzvah study was to learn the Hebrew blessings which Joseph would say when he was called up to the pulpit to listen to the reading of the Torah. The rabbi showed him the scroll of the Torah and opened it to the Book of Leviticus. He read from Chapter 19, which would be read on the

Sabbath of Joseph's Bar Mitzvah. He went over some of the laws. They were good laws that told how a man should treat his neighbor. They explained that he should be fair and honest.

The rabbi told Joseph what else he had to do on his Bar Mitzvah morning. He would say the Hebrew blessings for the Haftoro reading. Then he would read the passage from the Prophet Amos.

Joseph and the rabbi talked about the Prophet Amos. It seemed to Joseph that he was getting to know the prophet very well. He was almost like a friend, an older friend. Joseph knew that the prophet loved the people of Israel and was sorry when they did wrong. Amos hoped he could make them understand how God wanted them to be just and kind to their fellow men.

The six months sped by fast. Joseph learned his Hebrew blessings. He practiced the English readings. He read a book about the Prophet Amos. He talked with the rabbi about the Torah. He learned how many of the laws of the Torah would help him to become a fine man as well as a good Jew. He knew there was much more for him to learn. He was ready to become Bar Mitzvah—a Son of the Commandment.

Joseph's Bar Mitzvah

Everyone was proud of Joseph. He had had a fine Bar Mitzvah. He stood up in the temple on the pulpit and recited the blessings over the Torah. Then Joseph explained in English what he would read from the Torah. He read it loud and clear. Everyone in the temple could hear him. Before the Torah was put back into the Ark, Joseph read the Haftoro. He recited the Hebrew blessings. He read the wonderful verses from the Book of Amos which he had studied so carefully.

Hillel sat in the temple with Mother and Father and Leah. Nearby were Grandma and Grandpa, and many aunts and uncles and cousins. They had come from near and from far to Joseph's Bar Mitzvah.

When Joseph read, "Are ye not as the children of the Ethiopians to Me, O Children of Israel?" Hillel remembered what the rabbi had told him and Joseph about God's love for all people. He was sure that Joseph would never forget his Bar Mitzvah. He was sure they would both remember the lesson which Amos had taught so many years before.

146

The rabbi called Mother and Father to the pulpit. Hillel moved over and held Leah's hand tightly. How exciting it was to hear the rabbi bless Joseph, and bless Mother and Father, too. All of them, everyone in the family, would remember Joseph's Bar Mitzvah.

The Sabbath services were over. Mother and Father hurried home. The whole family was having a Sabbath lunch together at home. Mother had to see that everything was ready.

Hillel and Joseph walked home more slowly.

"The temple was full of our friends and relatives," said Hillel. "I did not know we had so many, did you?"

"No," said Joseph. "And everyone was very good to me. I received so many presents. That is one thing the rabbi did not talk about. Some of the presents were real surprises. It seems as if everyone was happy with me."

"Oh, my," said Hillel. "I almost forgot. Aunt Lottie and Uncle Milton cannot come to lunch. They had to go home. They gave me a letter for you." He took the letter from his coat pocket and handed it to Joseph.

Joseph stopped in the middle of the street. He opened the letter and began to read it. His eyes

147

148

opened wide. "Listen to this," he cried. This is what the letter said:

Dear Joseph:

Congratulations on your Bar Mitzvah. Uncle Milton and I are very proud of you. We heard how hard you studied. We want to give you a present.

We are sending you some money. You may do as you please with this money. You may put it in the bank to have when you grow older. You may buy something with it now. You may share some of it with other boys and girls who do not have as many good things as you do.

With love,
Aunt Lottie and Uncle Milton

Hillel and Joseph looked at each other. "That is very nice of Aunt Lottie and Uncle Milton. You can think of something you really want to buy."

"There is something else in the letter," said Joseph. "Aunt Lottie is right. A Bar Mitzvah is a good time for sharing. I have received many gifts. I have pens and pencils, wallets and key-chains, books and a brief case. Of course, there are lots of other things I'd like to have."

"Did you receive money or checks from someone else?"

"Oh, yes," said Joseph. "I gave everything to Mother. She is holding the money for me. I will have to think over what Aunt Lottie said."

149

"You will have to think about sharing," said Hillel.

"You mean keep part of the gifts for myself and give the rest to other boys and girls? That's not very good. There won't be much for anyone."

"That is what we do with our Keren Ami money at religious school," Hillel answered. "We do not have very much money. When it is all collected at the end of the year, we have a meeting. We learn who needs help. We decide where our money should go. We send it away. Other schools send money, too. When it is all added up there is enough to help many children."

"Now I understand," said Joseph. "There may be other Bar Mitzvah boys who will share their gifts. It would be good if each one of us would give something."

"If you share your gifts," Hillel exclaimed, "your money can travel far away. Some of it can help children in America. Some of it can go to Europe, and some of it to the State of Israel. The boys who share their gifts will celebrate their Bar Mitzvah all over the whole wide world."

"I will ask Mother and Father to help me decide how to divide my presents. Now, let's hurry. I will be late for my own party."

Joseph and Hillel hurried home. Leah met them at the door. "How slow you are," she scolded. "Everyone is waiting for you." Then she dropped her voice to a whisper. "And there are many new presents waiting for you, Joseph."

Joseph and Hillel looked at each other. They began to laugh. They laughed and laughed. Leah didn't understand. She would have to wait for an explanation.

151

An Independence Day

Hillel and Joseph were walking home from religious school.

"I must look at my luach as soon as I get home," said Hillel.

"You are always busy with your luach," answered Joseph. "What are you looking for now?"

"I have to find out the English date for the 5th of Iyor," replied Hillel.

Joseph kept silent. He wondered what was happening on the 5th of Iyor. He knew that Hillel wanted him to ask. But he had his own luach. He decided to look for himself.

The boys ran up the stairs as they entered the house. They went into their rooms. Hillel's luach was on his desk. In a moment he found the date— the 5th of Iyor. Yes, it was in red. It was a holiday. The English date was the 13th of May.

Mother called, "Time for lunch." Hillel picked up his luach and opened his door. As he stepped out of his room, Joseph's door opened, too. In Joseph's hand was his luach.

"Does your luach tell what happens on the 5th of Iyor?" asked Hillel.

"Yes," Joseph replied. "It is Independence Day for the State of Israel."

"That's what Miss Aviva told us. It is like the Fourth of July for us in America. We are going to have a celebration in class. Miss Aviva gave each one of us something to do for the celebration."

"What must you do?" asked Joseph, as they walked down the stairs.

"She asked me to draw a chart or a picture about the State of Israel and America. Some of the boys and girls are singing songs, and some will recite poems or tell a story. I would like to think of something very special."

All week long Hillel was thinking about the Israeli Independence Day. He asked questions. He spoke to Mother and Father. He walked over to the library. He found a book about the State of Israel. He met his cousin David and talked to him. He read some pages in his American history book. He asked the rabbi some questions, too.

On Thursday afternoon Hillel was very busy. He had many things to do. First he went to the supermarket. He asked for a large carton. He carried home the carton. Then he went into the kitchen.

153

Mother was not at home, but Hillel knew what he needed. He found a roll of wide, white shelf paper. After that he went into the library and opened Father's desk. He knew what he wanted there, too. It was a roll of scotch tape. He had everything else he needed in his own room.

But Hillel was mistaken. He needed one more thing. He needed help. He could not do this job alone. He would ask Joseph and Leah to help.

Joseph and Leah were drinking milk and eating cookies.

"Will you help me?" Hillel asked.

"What are you doing?"

"I am making something for Independence Day."

"Independence Day!" exclaimed Leah. "Why do you need help now? The Fourth of July will not come until the summertime."

Hillel laughed. "Do you think our country is the only country in the world? Other countries have an Independence Day, too."

"Oh," said Leah, "I never thought of that."

Joseph explained like a big brother. "Hillel means the State of Israel's Independence Day. That takes place in May this year."

"Come up into my room," begged Hillel. "I will show you what I have."

The three children ran up the stairs. They saw the large carton and the shelf paper. They saw the scotch tape together with a package of crayons which Hillel had laid out. Next to them was a pair of sharp scissors. On his desk was a tablet and a collection of pictures.

Leah ran over to the carton. She climbed inside. Only her head peeped out.

"Come on in," she cried. "We can play house here."

"Leah, you are too little to help. You just want to play."

"No, no," she cried. "I can help. I will be a big girl. Tell me what to do." She climbed out of the carton.

Joseph took charge. "First tell us your idea, Hillel."

"Could we make a big chart to tell things about America and about the State of Israel? They are like each other in many ways. I read about them. I have written some of them down." He picked up the tablet from his desk.

Joseph studied the paper carefully. Hillel

155

watched him. He hoped Joseph would like his idea.

"You must also put down how they are different," Joseph declared.

"I know that," cried Leah. "America is big and the State of Israel is little. See, I have helped already."

Joseph and Hillel laughed. "Let's begin," they said.

Hillel and Leah held the carton steady. Joseph began to cut out one side of the carton. He worked slowly and carefully.

"Now we will cover it with Mother's good white shelf paper."

They fitted the shelf paper over the cardboard. They smoothed it down and fastened it with the scotch tape.

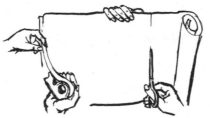

"Let's begin on your list," Joseph said. "I will read it off to you and you can print it." Hillel had learned how to print at art school. He did it very well. Across the top he wrote:

UNITED STATES — STATE OF ISRAEL
— HOW · THEY · ARE · ALIKE —

1. PEOPLE HAVE COME TO THEM FROM ALL PARTS OF THE WORLD.
2. THEIR PEOPLE LOVE THE BIBLE.
3. EVERY CITIZEN MAY VOTE.
4. THEY EACH HAVE A PRESIDENT.
5. THEY FOUGHT FOR LIBERTY.
6. THERE IS A DESERT IN EACH COUNTRY.
7. WONDERFUL FRUITS LIKE ORANGES AND GRAPES GROW IN EACH COUNTRY.

"I think I should leave some room for the class to put in some of their ideas," said Hillel. "And Miss Aviva can help us, too."

"Now let's see how they are different," said Joseph. "Write down two headings, and then we can begin with what Leah said."

157

Hillel printed with different colored crayons.

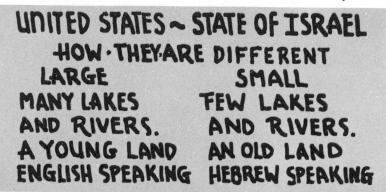

UNITED STATES ~ STATE OF ISRAEL
HOW · THEY·ARE DIFFERENT
LARGE   SMALL
MANY LAKES   FEW LAKES
AND RIVERS.   AND RIVERS.
A YOUNG LAND   AN OLD LAND
ENGLISH SPEAKING   HEBREW SPEAKING

Then Hillel printed three more lines across the bottom. It said:

~GOOD LUCK ~
TO THE STATE OF ISRAEL
FROM THE
UNITED STATES OF AMERICA

Leah looked at the chart. "It is too plain," she said. "Where are the pictures?"

The children selected some of the pictures which Hillel had ready. They pasted them on. Then Leah said, "Wait a minute. I have something else." She ran out of the room and soon returned. In her hands were a package of colored decals for decoration. They brightened up the chart. It looked much better. Leah really had helped.

158

"Let me carry the chart to school," said Leah.

"It is too big and heavy for any of us to carry," said Hillel. "We shall have to ask Daddy to drive us to religious school on Sunday."

Joseph had an idea. "We will ask him to put down the top of the car. The three of us will sit in the back seat and hold the chart. It will have a proud trip to school."

A Task for Hillel

Hillel's luach was getting top-heavy. It stood on Hillel's desk like a little tent, with pages coming down in the front and in the back. Each month Hillel turned a page over.

Now the year was almost gone. The holiday of Shovuos was coming. When Hillel turned the page of the luach it fell back with a click. That was because it was heavier in back than in front. Shovuos came in the month of Sivon. There were only three months left to the year. That meant only a few more pages to turn over.

Hillel looked at the new page of the luach. The 6th of Sivon was red for Shovuos. Some calendars showed Shovuos on two days, the 6th and the 7th, because Orthodox Jews celebrate the holiday for two days. But this was an Israeli calendar. In the Land of Israel the pilgrim festivals were celebrated for only one day, the way Jews had done in ancient days. Hillel knew that Reform Jews celebrate the holiday for one day like the Jews in the Land of Israel.

Hillel needed help. He had promised to write a Shovuos story for his school paper. He knew two Shovuos stories that he could write about, but he was afraid that everyone else knew them, too. He remembered them from last year. They were the story of the giving of the Law on Mount Sinai and the story of Ruth. Wasn't there another Shovuos story— a new one?

Where would he find such a story? He thought and thought. Then his eyes brightened. Stories were in books. Books were in the library. The library was in religious school. He would go to school and ask the librarian to help him.

Hillel was right. The librarian gave him two books. He sat down to read them. The first book was all about the Bible. It told about the Ten Commandments. It told the story of Ruth. He had to look further.

The second book was full of Jewish legends and fables. They were old stories, but they were new to Hillel. He settled down to read. Just as he found the story he wanted, the librarian came over to him. "It is time to go home," she said. "We are closing the library. You may take the book home with you and finish it there."

On the way home Hillel went over the story

in his mind. He had another idea. He would draw a picture to go with it. Perhaps his story would be on the front page of the school paper.

Hillel worked on his story for three days. The first day he wrote it. He wrote slowly and carefully. The second day he read it over. He made changes. He crossed out words. He put in new and better ones. On the third day he copied his story on a clean sheet of paper. He drew a picture at the beginning and at the end. He was pleased with it. He hoped the editor of the paper would like his story.

Would you like to read Hillel's story? Here it is.

God's Holy Mountain

This is not a true story. It is a legend. That means it is a story which people began to tell each other long ago. No one knows who told it first.

I think that when the Children of Israel came to Canaan, a little boy said, "Tell me a story."

His father answered, "When our fathers were in the desert, they heard the thunder rumbling over the mountains. One man said to another, 'The mountains are speaking.' Everyone looked up at the mountains. Their tops were high in the clouds. The people thought, 'The mountains are speaking to God.' Then there came a loud clap of thunder. Someone else said, 'God is answering them.'"

What were the mountains saying? They heard that something wonderful was going to happen. God was giving the Torah to the Children of Israel. Moses was about to climb to the top of a mountain to receive the Torah and the Ten Commandments from God.

Which mountain would be chosen? Would it be the great, majestic Mt. Hermon? Its top was cov-

163

ered with snow and it reached high into the heavens. Would it be Mt. Carmel in the north of Palestine, or Mt. Tabor in the valley?

Each mountain spoke for itself. "Choose me!" "Choose me!" "Choose me!" "I am high!" "I am mighty!" "I am grand!"

God looked at the proud mountains. They trembled in fear and hope. Then God spoke.

"I will not choose a mountain that is proud because it is high and reaches to the clouds. I will choose a low mountain that is modest and does not dare to ask. This mountain served me once before. Near it, Moses saw the burning bush. My holy mountain shall be Mt. Sinai."

The mountains listened. They understood. To be quiet and wait for the word of God was better than to cry aloud and expect favors. They were ashamed.

God spoke again. "I am not angry with you. You wished to be chosen for a great honor. You wished to be blessed with the giving of the Law. That is not wrong. I am pleased that you wanted to be chosen. There are other days in Jewish history for each of you."

Mt. Tabor listened as its name was called. "A day will come," spoke the Voice of God, "when a

165

strong army will come against the Israelites. There will be a battle along the mountainside. Deborah, a judge in Israel, will lead the soldiers to victory. You, Mt. Tabor, shall see it."

Now it was the turn of Mt. Carmel. "For you, Mt. Carmel, there will be a different victory. The Prophet Elijah will battle with the false priests of Baal. On Mt. Carmel, he will prove that the idols are false. He will lead the Israelites back to their own God."

What of Mt. Hermon? The legend doesn't say. God gave it great beauty. It shines like a great jewel for miles and miles. That must be its reward.

And Mt. Sinai? Moses received the Torah on Mt. Sinai. From that day forth it has been called the holy mountain. It was too humble to ask, but God remembered it and chose it.

✴   ✴   ✴

Hillel's story *was* chosen to be on page one of the school paper. He gave it a good name. He called it "God's Holy Mountain."

The Best Holiday

The boys could not agree. Each one had a different idea.

Hillel said, "I have looked through my whole luach. I have thought about every holiday. I cannot decide which I like the best. I cannot decide which Jewish holiday is the most important. What do you say, Joseph?"

"I say Passover is the best and the most important. Who did more than Moses for the Hebrews? What is more exciting than the story of how they became free? And what a lot of fun we have at the Seder."

Stanley said, "I like Chanuko. No holiday is better. Mother and Dad and I celebrate it together. It is my family holiday." Hillel remembered the first night of Chanuko. He knew why Stanley liked Chanuko so much. But he wasn't satisfied. "I shall wait. Shovuos will soon be here. Then we shall have celebrated all the important holidays of the year. Perhaps I can decide then."

Hillel's luach told him he had three more days to

167

wait for Shovuos. On the fourth morning, everyone was up early. The children did not go to school. Father did not go to work. Mother had very little to do in the house. She had prepared everything for the holiday on erev Shovuos. The family was going to temple together. The boys and girls in the tenth grade would be confirmed during services. Joseph and Hillel knew many of the pupils in the Confirmation class. Mother and Father had many friends among their parents.

The temple was very full. It was decorated with greens and with flowers. The service began. The wide doors in the rear opened. Two by two, the Confirmation class walked slowly down the center aisle. The boys and girls had serious faces. They had been studying all year for this important day.

All the students took part in the services. They assisted the rabbi. They read from the prayer book. Then the Ark was opened. Hillel noticed that the Scrolls of the Law had white covers instead of the red velvet ones they usually wore on Sabbath. "That must be for the holiday," he thought.

Three Confirmation boys stood up for the Torah services. The first boy opened the Ark and took out the Torah. The second one carefully took off the white silk cover. He recited the blessing before the reading from the Torah. The third boy was the one who would read from the Torah. First he explained what he would read.

"On Shovuos," he said, "we celebrate the giving of the Law on Mt. Sinai. The Bible tells us that God gave the Ten Commandments to Moses and he brought them to the Children of Israel. It was a gift to the Children of Israel, but it was also a gift to all the people of the world. This happened more than three thousand years ago. Today, after so many years, we boys and girls who will be confirmed today receive the Torah once again. Our rabbi, our teachers and our parents pass it on to us. We promise to love it as they do, and to follow its teachings." He waited for a moment. He gave his classmates a chance to think over what he had said. He was speaking for them. Then he went on, "Now I shall read the Ten Commandments in Hebrew from our wonderful Torah."

Hillel knew about the Ten Commandments. His Shovuos story was about Mt. Sinai, and how it was chosen to receive the Torah. He listened carefully. He wished he could understand the Hebrew words. He was glad when one of the girls read the Ten Commandments in English. That helped everyone to understand them. And then something very

169

nice happened. Everyone in the temple, young and old, stood up and said the Ten Commandments. Even Leah followed the words as he pointed them out to her. It was almost like standing at Mt. Sinai.

The Torah was put away. The Confirmation class stood at the altar. The temple was quiet. One of the girls was speaking.

"There is a second part to the holiday of Shovuos. It is a spring harvest festival. It is the festival of first-fruits. That is why there are greens and flowers in our synagogue. In Bible times, the farmers brought their offerings to the Temple. Their best fruits were set aside for the offerings. That is how they thanked God for His blessings."

Hillel was thinking hard. He was glad he had waited for Shovuos. It was a fine holiday. It celebrated the giving of the Torah. It celebrated the spring harvest. These came from the Shovuos of long ago. And now, something else belonged to Shovuos, something that was new—Confirmation.

Some day he would be confirmed. Of course, he would have to wait a long time—almost eight years. Joseph would only have three more years to wait. He listened to the boys and girls of the Confirmation class. They were reciting together, *Sh'ma Yisroel,*

Adonoi Elohenu Adonoi Echod.—"Hear, O Israel, the Lord our God, the Lord is One." Hillel said that prayer every Shabos morning and every night when he said his prayers. But the boys and girls who were being confirmed were saying it for a special reason. On this day, they wanted to be counted as Jews among all Jews all over the world.

The service was almost over. The rabbi blessed the boys and girls of the Confirmation class. Their eyes were shining as they left the altar. They held their heads high. Their parents watched proudly as they walked down the long aisle.

Hillel made up his mind. Outside of the temple, he waited for Joseph and Stanley.

"Have you changed your minds about the holidays?" he asked.

"No," said Joseph.

"No," said Stanley.

"I guess every holiday is important. But I thought of something new this morning. Shovuos is important for boys and girls. We will be confirmed on Shovuos. It is really our holiday more than any of the others."

Mother and Father were listening. Father laughed. "This is an argument no one will win," he said. "The holidays come year after year. Each one is good and has a meaning of its own. They all bring us joy. Let's decide to like them all."

At last the boys agreed. Father was right. But deep down in his heart, Stanley liked Chanuko the best, Joseph liked Passover the best, and Hillel still liked Shovuos the best of all.

Standards and Banners

Hillel looked up at the enormous grandstand. He had never seen such a large crowd before. Some people were already sitting in the grandstand. Others were walking toward it and some were even running. They were all trying to find a good seat to watch the parade.

Father was a veteran. He received tickets for seats in the grandstand. When the tickets came, everyone was excited. Hillel counted the days. He checked them off on his calendar: June 10, June 11, June 12, June 13, and at last June 14—Flag Day.

The grandstand was decorated with red, white, and blue bunting. Flags flew from every side.

Father, Joseph, and Hillel had seats together. Mother and Leah sat one row further down, just in front of them. They could all see very well.

From far down the avenue came the sound of music. The parade was beginning. Hillel strained his eyes. He could hardly see a thing. But as he listened, the sounds grew stronger. The music became plain. He recognized the melody. It was one he

173

sang in school. The first band came into sight.

How fine the players looked, with bright blue uniforms and yellow bands across their chests. The drummers beat the heavy drums. The shining brass trumpets and horns rang out together. People were singing with the music. Hillel sang, too.

Then came the parade of the flags, one after another. In the lead were two American flags. One was a copy of the first flag of the United States. It had thirteen stars. The other was the newest flag of our country, with fifty stars. The parade halted in front of the grandstand. The music stopped. Everyone stood up. On the front row of the grandstand stood the mayor. He placed his hand over his heart. He began to recite the pledge of allegiance. Everyone joined him, "I pledge allegiance to the flag of the United States of America and to the republic for which it stands, one nation under God, indivisible, with liberty and justice for all."

All was quiet for a moment. Then the big bass drum boomed out and the parade went on again. Flag after flag was carried aloft—the state flag, flags of the regiments, flags of many nations. The police band passed by. The fireman's band played proudly.

Father explained everything to Hillel and

Joseph. He recognized the different flags. He named them all.

"Why does the flag give us such a funny feeling inside?" asked Hillel.

"It is not the flag that does that," said Father. "It is because the flag stands for something. When you see the American flag go by, you are proud and happy. You think of the people who are working together to make this a fine country to live in. You think of teachers, of doctors, of builders, of farmers, and of scientists. You think of soldiers, too, who may give their lives for their land. You want to serve your country, too. I am sure you will find your own way when you are older."

The parade was almost over. But there was one more band and one more flag. It was different from all the others. Hillel could not remember if he had seen it before. "What flag is that?" he asked.

Father knew that one, too. "That is the flag of the United Nations," he answered.

"I know about the United Nations," said Hillel. "We celebrated United Nations Day in school. Do you remember?" he asked Joseph.

"Yes, it was in October. We carried the United Nations flag into our school assembly."

"The United Nations tries to keep the world at

peace," said Father. "People from countries all over the world come together during the year. If there is trouble in some part of the world they are ready to help."

"No more wars?" asked Hillel.

"That is what we hope for. Perhaps the United Nations will make that possible. In the meantime, it is helping men and women and boys and girls all over the world to lead better and happier lives."

The parade was over. The last flag had passed by. The music of the last band came from far off. Father and the boys joined Mother and Leah.

Leah had a question to ask. It seemed that Leah always had a question to ask.

"Daddy, who had the first flag—the very first flag?"

Father laughed. "That is hard to say. Men carried banners and flags long, long ago."

Joseph had something to say. "When Columbus came to America, he placed the flag of Spain on the shore. That is how he claimed the New World for Spain."

Mother was holding Leah's hand very tightly. They were walking down the steps slowly. "Let us sit down for a little while," said Mother. "Some people are pushing. One of us may fall."

They all sat down. Father said, "That's right, Joseph. But that was only five hundred years ago."

"Were there flags before that?" asked Leah.

"Oh, yes," answered Father. "Even the Bible talks about banners. There is a psalm that says, 'In the name of our God, we will set up our banners.'"

"How far back does that go?" asked Hillel.

"That verse is very old," said Father. "It was probably sung almost three thousand years ago."

Joseph repeated, "Banners in the name of God. That sounds good."

"Does the Bible say anything else about flags?" asked Leah.

"Yes," said Father. "You remember that the Children of Israel were divided into twelve tribes. When they lived in the wilderness, each tribe camped together. And it seems—"

"That each tribe had its own flag!" Hillel interrupted.

"You are right. The Bible says that each tribe set up a camp with its own standard. A standard is another word for flag."

"Each tribe must have had its own Betsy Ross," Joseph laughed.

Mother looked around. "I think we can walk

down now," she said. "The crowd is thinning out. No one is pushing."

They walked down the rest of the steps and reached the car.

Hillel said, "I didn't think we would talk about the Bible on Flag Day."

Mother answered, "Most Americans love the Bible. Jews and Christians study it, and follow its teachings."

"Long ago," said Father, "a wise rabbi said, 'Look in the Bible and look again. You will find everything in it'—even flags. Flag Day is a very good day to talk about the Bible."

The Quarrel

Hillel was away from home. He was at a summer camp. He belonged to the sophomore group. The boys in this group were from nine to eleven years old. It was Hillel's first summer at camp. Joseph was in the camp, too. It was his second summer. Leah was at home with Mother and Father.

At first everything was very strange. Hillel slept in a cabin with five other boys and a counselor. The counselor's name was Adam. Each boy had a small cupboard next to his cot for his clothes. At the foot of the cot, each had his low camp trunk. It made a good seat.

Hillel had a new friend. His name was Benjy. His cot was next to Hillel's. Benjy was an old camper. He had been coming to camp for three seasons. He had blond hair and blue eyes. Benjy was very lively and curious. He asked Hillel about his home and his family. The other campers were named Eddie and Bob and Josh and Saul.

The boys were unpacking their trunks. Hillel was trying to find a place for everything he had brought along. He put his clothes into the cupboard. He hung his tennis racquet on the wall between two large nails. He placed his books on top of the cup-board. Then he had to find a place for his luach.

Should he put it inside the cupboard, or should he stand it on top next to his books? Perhaps he should hang it on the wall just below the tennis racquet. There was a small nail he could use. He tried both places. The top of the cupboard wasn't very even. The luach fell down. He hung it on the wall. That was better.

181

"What is that?" someone asked. Hillel looked up. Bob stood next to him.

"That's a luach," Hillel explained. "It's a Hebrew calendar but it shows the English months and the Hebrew months, too."

"What do you need that for in camp?" asked Bob. "I think that's a silly thing to bring to camp."

Before Hillel could answer, Benjy came over. Bob turned to him.

"Look what Hillel brought to camp! Who needs a Hebrew calendar here?" he asked. "Anyway, there aren't any Jewish holidays in the summer-time."

"Don't pay any attention to Bob," said Benjy. "He always starts up with the new boys."

"I don't care," said Hillel. "But I don't see why I can't bring anything I like to camp. Anyway, I'm sure there must be some important Jewish days during the summer. Here, look for yourself."

Benjy turned the pages of the luach. "Here's a day marked in red—the 9th of Ov. Say, that's Tisho B'Ov. I remember that from last year. We put on a program about it last summer. It was about the Temple in Jerusalem, and how it was destroyed by the Romans. I was the Captain of the Guard." He put the luach on Hillel's cupboard.

"We don't need Hillel's calendar for that," Bob

kept on. "The English calendar is good enough for me." He reached for the luach. But Hillel was too quick for him.

"I'll keep my luach and I'll put it wherever I want," he declared. "You don't have to look at it."

The other boys had gathered around. The cabin was in a hub-bub.

"What's going on here?" a new voice asked. Adam came into the cabin. All the boys spoke at once. Adam heard, "Hillel, Bob, luach, Tisho B'Ov." At last he understood.

"This is pretty important," he said. "I'm not talking about the luach. I'm talking about your rights. Does Hillel have the right to bring a luach into our bunk if Bob doesn't like it? Does Bob have the right to stop Hillel? When do we say to a fellow, 'You can't do this'?"

Benjy spoke right up. "I think you can do what you want to do, as long as you don't interfere with the other boys."

"I agree," said Saul. "If Hillel had a bell and he rang it at night after we went to sleep, we'd have the right to stop him."

"You get the idea," said Adam.

"Let's take a vote," someone said.

"Are you ready?" Adam asked. "Remember,

183

we're not voting on the luach. We're voting on Hillel's, or anyone else's, right to have a luach, or a book, or even a bell."

The boys voted. Hillel didn't vote. It was four to one. No one sided with Bob.

Adam picked up the luach. "This looks like a pretty useful thing to have around," he said. "Let's try it out. Why, here, on the first page, there is a date for us to observe this very week. Who knows it?"

That was easy. All the boys shouted, "The Fourth of July."

Adam went on. "I'm sure we will use the calendar again and again during the summer."

He gave the luach back to Hillel. "Put your luach wherever you please. No one will disturb it."

The boys finished their unpacking. Hillel was tired. He lay down on his bunk. No one disturbed him.

Later on he went with the other sophs to the center of the campus to see the flag being lowered.

Benjy explained, "In the evening we have flag-lowering. Each one of us has a turn to take part in the ceremony."

Everything was new to Hillel. He was very quiet. He was learning how to be a camper.

Then came the last lesson of the day—taps. The

boys went outside. They stood about in a large circle. It was dark. The hills nearby were large and shadowy. The stars shone brightly above. From afar came the sound of the bugler. The boys joined arms at their shoulders and swayed as they sang together:

Day is done,
Gone the sun,
From the hills,
From the sea,
From the sky.
All is well,
Safely rest,
God is nigh.

Hillel swayed with the circle of boys. The song ended. He was ready to drop his arms. But Benjy was holding one arm fast.

He turned around. On the other side, Benjy was holding fast to Bob. He looked from Hillel to Bob. "How about it?" he asked. "Why not be friends? Shake hands."

Bob stretched his hand across to Hillel. Hillel clasped his hand firmly. The quarrel was forgotten. It was good to have another friend.

185

Poor Richard

On Sunday morning Adam woke the boys up early. He did not wait for the morning bugle.

"Up!" he cried. "It's the Fourth of July. We have work to do. We must get ready for the regatta."

The boys jumped out of bed. They dressed quickly. They made their beds and swept the bunk. They did not fool around or waste time. When the call came for breakfast they were ready.

"Now," said Adam after breakfast, "we have saved a lot of time. Our bunk is ready for inspection. We can begin to plan for our part in the regatta."

Hillel was puzzled. "I don't know what the regatta is," he said.

"I'm sorry," said Adam. "I forgot. You are our only new boy. Bob, you tell Hillel about the regatta."

"A regatta is really a sailing contest," explained Bob. "But in camp we call our water festival a regatta. We celebrate the Fourth of July with a regatta. Each bunk decorates a rowboat or a canoe. We sail across the lake to the girls' camp. The girls

186

watch us. Next month we shall watch them at their water festival."

"I went to the costume house yesterday," said Adam. "I have some costumes and lots of crepe paper. How shall we use them?"

The boys had many ideas. Adam wrote them down on a pad. They were:

FIGHTING FOR FREEDOM

BUILDING AMERICA

GREAT MEN OF HISTORY

AMERICAN HEROES

Benjy said, "You have to have all kinds of people working together to do anything good. That's how our country grew. Let's think of some of the men we study about in American history."

"We can each decide on a man and dress up like him," one of the boys cried. "And then we'll decorate our rowboat."

It seemed like a good idea. The other boys agreed.

"I'll be George Washington, the soldier and our first President. He surely belongs on our float," said Bob.

"And I want to be Patrick Henry," called out Benjy. "He made a great speech for liberty."

187

"Good," said Adam. "That makes two. What will the rest of you do?"

Josh spoke up. "Wasn't there a man named Haym Salomon who helped George Washington?"

"Of course," Adam replied. "He gave the army money and food when they needed it most. He was a banker. And he was a Jew who loved his new country." He looked around. "What will you be, Eddie?"

"I'd like to be Nathan Hale. He was a brave patriot who died for his country."

It was Saul's turn.

"I am thinking of someone different," he said. "I would like to be Daniel Boone. He was a woodsman and explorer. He helped America grow."

The boys turned to Hillel. He was the only one left.

"What about you, Hillel?"

Before Hillel had a chance to answer, Adam said, "I know just the one for you to be, Hillel. Do you know what an almanac is?"

None of the boys knew. Neither did Hillel.

"An almanac is a calendar like your luach. It has the days and months of the year, but it often has more in it. It has wise sayings from many books. It tells farmers when to plant their seeds. It has advice for mothers and for fathers. There was a famous almanac in revolutionary days. It was called, 'Poor Richard's Almanac.' Does anyone know who Poor Richard was?"

Josh remembered. "Poor Richard was Benjamin Franklin."

Adam was pleased. "Good. Hillel, would you like to be Benjamin Franklin? He was a very wise man. He may even have known something about the Hebrew calendar."

Hillel was glad to be Benjamin Franklin. He thought that when he came home from camp he would find out more about Poor Richard and his almanac.

Adam said, "We have a soldier, a speaker, a banker, a patriot, a woodsman and a writer—each did his share for our country."

The boys sorted out the costumes. They found jacket and pants to wear. Adam helped them make cocked hats out of cardboard and crepe paper. He found a coonskin cap for Daniel Boone. Each boy printed a sign with his name. Then they went down to the waterfront. They found their rowboat. Sam gave them red, white, and blue bunting and an American flag. They decorated the boat. They painted a sign and put it across the boat on poles. It said, "All together for the U.S.A."

The morning went very fast. After lunch there was a short rest period. Then the boys put on their costumes. Adam put a red crepe paper sash across the front of Hillel's coat. He found some tin medals. He said, "After the Revolution, Benjamin Franklin went to France for our country. When he stood before the king, he must have worn a sash and some medals."

The boys put on their hats. They walked down to the waterfront to wait their turn.

The regatta began. The boats and the canoes started off. The first one had the biggest campers. They were dressed like Indians, with feathered headdresses and painted faces. One boat had flags of many nations. One boat carried "Moses and the Ten Commandments." Red, white, and blue streamers floated in the air. There was singing and shouting as the boats crossed the lake.

Adam rowed for his boys. They came to the girls' camp. The girl campers were sitting along the beach. It was decorated with American flags. Adam rowed very slowly. The boat hardly moved. The boys stood up and showed their signs, one by one. The girls clapped their hands for them. Then it was time for the next float. Adam rowed away.

He brought the boat near the beach. They waited for the rest of the regatta to pass by.

At last it was all over. The boys in the canoes and rowboats joined the girls on the beach in song. They sang their favorite songs—songs of America, campfire songs, Hebrew songs.

One by one the boats went back across the lake. Hillel and his bunkmates were happy. They were satisfied with their float.

They came near the dock. One by one they stepped out. Suddenly Hillel noticed Joseph. He called and waved. That was a mistake. He missed his step. Instead of stepping on to the dock, he stepped right into the water.

Adam fished him out in a minute. He was not hurt. But what happened? The colors in the crepe paper began to run. The red sash and the blue cocked hat mixed together. The medals floated away. Hillel's face turned red and blue.

The boys began to laugh. They could not help themselves. "Poor Hillel," cried Benjy.

Hillel had a good answer. He did not mind. "Not poor Hillel," he called. "Poor Richard!"

Another New Year

Summer was over. Labor Day had come and gone. School had begun.

Things were happening at home. Fresh, starched curtains were hung on the windows. The rugs were cleaned and the floors were waxed. The house shone from top to bottom.

Mother was busy in the kitchen. She was baking honey cake. That was a sure sign. Rosh Ha-shono was only a few days off.

Hillel's room was very neat. He had thrown away all his old papers. Only last year's luach was still on his desk. It was turned to the last page. That was the best sign that the year was almost over.

Hillel picked up the luach and held it in his hand. He turned it over. Then he made a discovery. The back cover of the luach had some printing on it. He looked at it carefully. It was an order form. This is what it said:

Dear sir:

If you wish to order a copy of this calendar for the coming year, fill in the next line.

Please send me ＿＿ copies of the Israeli Calendar. Price, $1.00 each.

NAME ＿＿＿＿＿＿＿＿＿＿＿＿＿＿＿＿＿

ADDRESS ＿＿＿＿＿＿＿＿＿＿＿＿＿＿＿

＿＿＿＿＿＿＿＿＿＿＿＿＿＿＿

Hillel flew downstairs. He ran into the kitchen and showed Mother the card. "May I send for three more copies of the luach for next year?" he asked. "We don't have to go down to the Jewish bookstore. Mr. Levine will mail them to us."

"That is a good way to start the New Year," said Mother. "Fill out the card and order three copies. I will give you a check for them. They will be Rosh Ha-shono presents for you and Joseph and Leah."

Hillel carefully removed the back cover from the luach. He filled in the order and wrote down his name and address. He addressed an envelope to Mr. Levine. He felt very grown up.

Hillel picked up his luach. He let the pages slide through his fingers. "I have a whole year in my hand," he said. "All the days and all the months—all the holidays and all the celebrations. If I look through the luach, I can remember all that we did during the year. I hate to throw it away."

Mother laughed. "You can throw away the luach, but you cannot throw away the year that has passed. That is a part of you already. When the new luach comes, it will start you off on a new year. I hope it will have lots of good days in it for all of us."

Hillel ran out of the kitchen. "I'll mail the letter," he said, "and we will be ready for Rosh Ha-shono and for the New Year."

Glossary and Pronouncing List

â—care ā—pay ă—bad ä—art ȧ—soda ē—me ĕ—bed
ē—fern ī—ice ĭ—tin ō—go ŏ—not ô—or ū—rule
u̇—unite ŭ—run

Adonoi—ä-dō-noy'—Lord
Amos—ā'-mŏs—A prophet in Israel
Aram—ă-räm'—A country north of ancient Israel
ato—ä-tô'—(art) Thou

boro—bô-rô'—(He) created
boruch—bô-rūch'—blessed
b'reshis—b'rā'-shēs—in the beginning

Carmel—cär'-mĕl—a mountain in Israel
chalil—chä-lēl'—a shepherd's pipe
chalo—chä-lô'—Sabbath loaf

Elohenu—ĕ-lō-hä'-nū—our God
Elohim—ĕ-lō-hēm'—God
esrog—ĕs'-rōg—citron, used during Sukos

ha—hä—the
Haggadah—hä-gä-dä'—book read at the Passover Seder
havdolo—häv-dô'-lô—prayer separating Sabbath from rest of the week

Josiah—jō-sī'-ȧ—a king of Judah

k'firim—k'-fī-rēm'—young lions
Kol Nidrei—kôl-nĭd-rā'—opening prayer of Yom Kippur eve

lamed—lä'-mĕd—a Hebrew letter

Levites—lē'-vīts—assistants to Temple priests
Leviticus—lĕ-vĭ'-tĭ-cŭs—third book of the Bible
luach—lū'-äch—calendar
lulov—lū-lôv'—palm leaf, used during Sukos

ma nishtano—mă-nĭsh-tä'-nô—how is this different?
melech—mĕ'-lĕch—king

olom—ō-lôm'—universe
orets—ô'-rĕts—earth

Pesach—pĕ'-säch—Passover

Rosh Ha-shono—rōsh'-hä-shô-nô'—New Year's Day

Seder—sā'-dĕr—meal and service for Passover eve
shamos—shä-môsh'—servant
shehecheyonu—shĕ-hĕ-chĕ-yô'-nū—who hast given us life
shomayim—shô-mä'-yĭm—heavens
Shovuos—shô-vū'-ōs—Festival of Giving of the Law
sofer—sō'-fâr—scribe

Tabor—tā'-bôr—a mountain in Judah
talis—tä'-lĭs—a prayer-shawl
tel—tĕl—a mound
t'filin—t'-fĭ-lēn'—phylacteries

195

Uzziah—û-zī-à'—A king of Judah

v'higionu—v'-hǐ-gĕ-ô'-nū
—and permitted us to reach

v'kiyimonu—v'-kǐ-yǐ-mô'-nū
—and preserved us

yod—yôd—hand, pointer

Yom Kippur—yōm kǐ-pūr'—Day
of Atonement

ze—zĕ—this

z'man—z'-män'—time

The Hebrew Months

NAME	USUALLY DURING
Tishri—tǐsh'-rē	September or October
Cheshvon—chĕsh'-vôn	November
Kislev—kǐs'-lāv	December
Teves—tā-vās'	December or January
Sh'vot—sh-vôt'	January
Ador—ä-dôr'	February or March
Nison—nǐ'-sôn	April
Iyor—ǐ'-yôr	May
Sivon—sǐ'-vôn	June
Tamuz—tä'-mūz	July
Ov—ôv	July or August
Elul—ĕ-lūl'	August or September

THE PUBLICATION OF THIS VOLUME
WAS MADE POSSIBLE BY THE ESTABLISH-
MENT OF A FUND FOR THE PUBLICATION
OF JEWISH RELIGIOUS SCHOOL LITERA-
TURE BY THE NATIONAL FEDERATION
OF TEMPLE SISTERHOODS

A ROOKIE READER

WHO IS WHO?

By Patricia C. McKissack

Illustrations by Elizabeth M. Allen

Prepared under the direction of Robert Hillerich, Ph.D.

CHILDRENS PRESS®
CHICAGO

*For Robert Lewis and
John Patrick McKissack*

Library of Congress Cataloging in Publication Data

McKissack, Patricia, 1944-
  Who is who?

  (A Rookie reader)
  Includes index.
  Summary: Even though Bobby and Johnny are twins, they often like opposite
things. Includes a word list.
  [1. Twins — Fiction. 2. English language — Synonyms and antonyms —
Fiction] I. Allen, Elizabeth, 1948-   ill. II. Title. III. Series.
PZ7.M478693Wh 1983   [E]   83-7361
ISBN 0-516-02042-0

12 13 14 15 16 17 18 19 20 R 99 98 97 96 95

Bobby and Johnny are twins.
Who is who?

3

This is Bobby.

This is Johnny.

Bobby looks like Johnny,
but Bobby is Bobby.

6

Johnny looks like Bobby,
but Johnny is Johnny.

Johnny likes red.

Bobby likes blue.

Who is who?

This is Johnny. This is Bobby.

Johnny likes hot.

Bobby likes cold.

Who is who?

This is Johnny. This is Bobby.

Johnny likes front.

Bobby likes back.

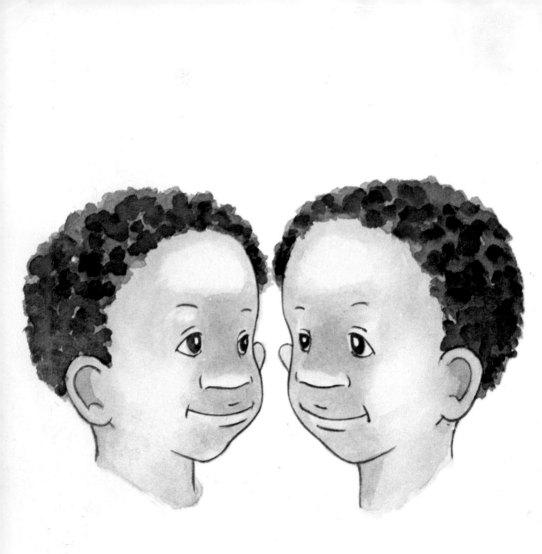

Who is who?

This is Johnny.

This is Bobby.

Johnny likes up.

Bobby likes down.

Who is who?

This is Johnny.   This is Bobby.

Johnny likes big.

Bobby likes little.

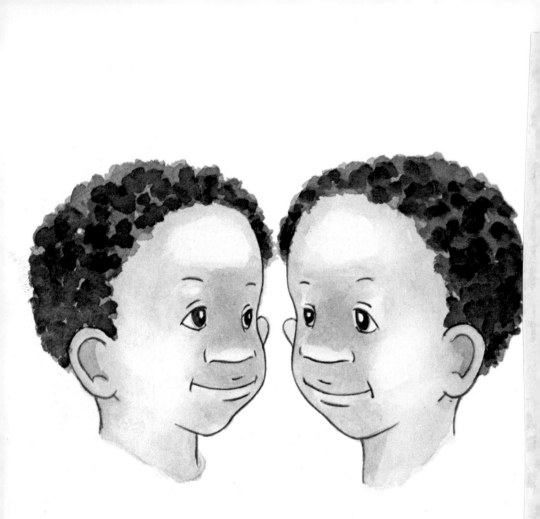

Who is who?

This is Johnny.   This is Bobby.

Johnny likes over.

Bobby likes under.

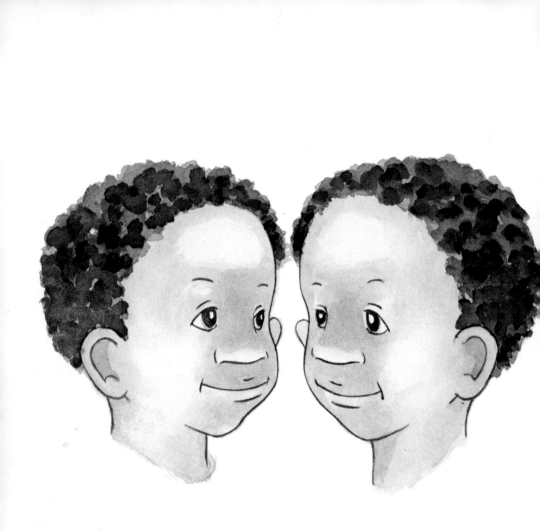

Who is who?

WORD LIST

and	Johnny
are	like, likes
back	little
big	looks
blue	over
Bobby	red
but	this
cold	twins
down	under
front	up
hot	who
is	

About the Author

Patricia C. McKissack is the president of All-Writing Services, a company that provides free-lance writing, editing, and teaching of writing to various businesses, industry, and educational facilities. Mrs. McKissack teaches a writing course at the University of Missouri-St. Louis, and conducts communication workshops throughout the country. *L Is For Listening* is a pre-school radio program designed to teach listening skills, she wrote and performed for KWMU Radio Station in St. Louis. Mrs. McKissack has a Masters Degree in Early Childhood Literature, and has written several books for children and adults. St. Louis is her home, where she enjoys gardening and growing roses with her husband and three children — Yes, she does have twins!

About the Artist

Elizabeth Allen is a free-lance children's illustrator. She spent her childhood in the Midwest. She studied fine art at St. Olaf College in Minnesota, and the University of Wisconsin at Madison, where she received her degree. Elizabeth lives with her husband Denby in Northbrook, Illinois. She has exhibited and sold her work, taught art to children, and has been a muralist. In addition to art, her greatest pleasures are composing and improvising music on the piano, and playing guitar and violin with her friends.